If Clouds Were Sheep

Sue Andrews

*A tale of sheep farming
in the Cotswolds*

Crumps Barn Studio

For my family

Crumps Barn Studio LLP
Crumps Barn, Syde, Cheltenham GL53 9PN
www.crumpsbarnstudio.co.uk

Cover images: Clouds © Tampatra1 / Dreamstime.com | Sheep and dog © Lorna Gray

Photographic plates © Sue Andrews | Lorna Gray | Mary Griese

ISBN 978-1-9998705-5-3

Prologue

I always say it started with Satan. To be fair, Satan wasn't all bad. In fact, he had a great sense of humour. Just a bit warped. He was dark and handsome, well muscled and fit. With a wicked grin, his brown eyes sparkled with delight every time he had a new idea. He also boasted a dangerous looking pair of horns that curled round on the top of his head, ending up with very sharp points facing slightly away from the front of his face, often directly at someone's leg.

For a Black Welsh Mountain Ram he was a superb specimen. However, Satan was one of those presents I wasn't sure we wanted. In fact, there were a number of occasions later when I was quite certain I didn't fully appreciate our gift.

Aubrey, on the other hand, was visualising the start of his first flock of sheep, so I stood little chance with any objections.

Contents

If Clouds Were Sheep

Chapter One

In the Beginning

Was it faith in ourselves or a flight of fancy that allowed us to dream of farming? We had no inherited farm, no livestock and very little money. My dream included horses. For Aubrey, farming was in his blood.

As a farm manager with no family farm to pass on, his father encouraged both his sons towards different careers. Aub qualified as an agricultural engineer, but his determination to farm never faltered, and in no time I was swept along on the same wave.

As a child I gazed longingly at the thoroughbred mares and foals grazing at the Jevington Stud on the South Downs, while Aubrey spent his holidays gathering sheep on the fells with his younger brother John, their uncle, cousins and local farmers and sons.

Family holidays were mainly spent on his aunt and uncle's farm near Kirkby Lonsdale, where they ran Dalesbred and Swaledale sheep. The promise of a warm sunny day, ideal for collecting for shearing, heralded an early start. The old Land Rover took them part way up the fell, but there was always at least another hour of upward trek before they started the descent, bringing the flock in.

Aubrey loved the sounds of the fells. The bleating of sheep, music from skylarks and the occasional mew of a buzzard, although that could herald a death. The breeze, however warm there was always a breeze. The dogs were magic. While occasional whistles were heard on the wind, the dogs worked from instinct and knowledge rather than instructions.

The raucous baas as ewes called lambs to stay close. This mob increased as ewes and lambs from further outlying runs joined the main flock heading down the valley, where they were sorted into those owned by his uncle and those of other farmers. His uncle's ewes had a blue paint mark on their left shoulder, while neighbouring farmers' stock may have a red mark in the same position or blue on the right shoulder, or black on the quarter; whatever colour and position they've used on that holding for centuries.

The rough grazing and craggy outcrops gently blended with a softer landscape as they neared the valley. At some point during the gather there would be time for the boys to stop and lie back on the course brittle grass to recover. His aunt would have sent him off with sandwiches and cake as would the other mothers.

They would scoop clear sparkling water into their hands from the small springs that appeared at intervals throughout the hills. Camaraderie was great but it was also fun to be on his own, with Moss, his uncle's older dog, at his side. He would tire more quickly than the younger dogs and be happy to walk alongside Aubrey as he wound his way down into the valley. Here Aubrey was master of the fell, flockmaster and sheepdog handler. On a warm summer day he rarely ceased smiling.

The sheep would gradually slow their pace, eventually running through a narrow sorting race, lined with high stone walls so none could escape, where they were divided into the separate flocks. It takes a smart man with a quick eye to work the shedding gate which turns the sheep to left or right depending on flock mark which has often faded. All ewes and most of the lambs will have been marked before turning on the hill after lambing, but occasionally an unmarked lamb, born on the fell, will come through and need sorting once it goes to its mother.

Next day's clipping was even more exhausting. First the ewes were run into the clipping shed while the lambs ran back into a field. The noise was unbelievable as lambs were separated from their mothers, but they soon settled down to graze. The ewes were caught from a pen, turned by twisting their neck to overbalance them, then set on their backside. They usually sat in this position quite happily as the shearer reached up, pulled the string to start the machine and removed their fleece.

The belly was clipped first, then the wool on the back leg opened out to the tail. Blades were thrust in long confident strokes against the sheep's skin. Each sweep of their shears took a full comb of wool from the body, while keeping the fleece as one whole piece.

Aubrey was entranced by the shearers. It took minutes or less to shear a hill ewe, then they were re-marked with their farm's smit mark and turned back to their lambs with little or no stress. Before his uncle, or whoever he was helping, brought the next ewe out of the pen, it was Aubrey's job to gather up the fleece thrown to one side of the clipping board; roll it into a ball, stretching and twisting the neck into a rope to secure the fleece as his uncle had shown him. He then threw it into the wool sacks, later climbing in and trampling down the fleeces so more could be packed in a bag. He had to be quick. No one would wait for him to falter; for fear of back strain no shearer wants to stand upright between sheep.

The sounds of ewes calling to lambs and lambs calling back

echoed across the valley. Eventually the motors would stop running and a picnic to surpass all others he'd ever seen was laid out in the barn on long trestle tables. Young boys could be clipped around the ear for sneaking a sausage roll in front of their seniors, but there was always plenty for everyone, washed down with endless mugs of tea. Aubrey often wondered how the shearers could bend over after such a lunch.

Later that summer both ewes and lambs would again be run through the stone lined race, this time into the deep circular trough used to dip them. He was again able to help with bringing the sheep off the fell and into the race, but his elders took over the dipping, plunging them into a foul-smelling grey liquid that would kill all the parasites the sheep were now carrying during the warm summer months. As they swam round looking for a way out, his uncle would poke them with a long metal pole, submerging them for longer than Aubrey thought was possible for them to hold their breath. Then to his relief they would clamber out of the dip and shake the excess off their wool.

"'As to be done lad, or they'd be eaten alive with maggots," he explained when Aubrey asked some of his many questions. "Flies lay eggs on their fleeces, especially the dirty bits round their back ends and when they hatch, them maggots live on sheep flesh if we don't do this to 'em."

One April, his uncle was ill at the start of lambing. Nearly fourteen, his mother agreed he could take the train to Kirkby Lonsdale and help his aunt and his young cousin with the lambing. Although others from neighbouring farms were taking turns helping out, it was a sharp learning curve for Aubrey. He walked for days on the in-bye fields checking that ewes and lambs were matched up and feeding well, his faithful friend Moss with him. Jack, from Far Fell, taught him to catch a ewe with a crook and tip her up so he could hold a daft lamb onto her teat to suckle. Once its stomach was full of milk it was content and seeing Moss lying down close by brought on a protective mothering ability to the young ewe.

"She'll sort it now," Jack told him as they moved on round the lambing fields to see what else needed assistance. Two weeks later, tired but incredibly happy he climbed on the train home assuring his aunt that he'd had the best Easter holiday possible.

Chapter Two

A Chance Meeting

Mine was a different childhood. We lived in the seaside town of Hastings in East Sussex. However, with country-loving parents, I probably saw almost as much of the countryside as Aubrey, with long days on the South Downs and some wonderful farm holidays.

Aged about nine I remember travelling to Saltash, just inside Cornwall, alongside the Tamar. The whole trip was an adventure. We would leave at four in the morning in our old black Austin and still not arrive at the farm B&B until early evening.

Farm life opened up a new world to me. The wonderful farmer and his wife treated us as family and apparently my parents had known them for years. Memories seep back of sitting on Mr Henwood's lap studying Farmers Weekly with him at every spare moment. With their grandson I collected eggs from the hen barns that ran above the pig sties, one day managing to drop the egg basket in with the big sow and litter beneath us.

Isaac said we mustn't go in with the pigs as they can be dangerous when they have young, but I was more afraid of having lost the eggs, so scrambled down into the sty, collected the basket of undamaged eggs that had fallen on the deep straw bedding, and clambered back up with Isaac's help, the sow just keeping a watchful eye on my intrusion, her babies tucked safely round her. Neither of us told anyone.

An only child, I'd never felt the need for siblings. The only thing I desperately wanted, like so many little girls, was a pony. Living in a top floor flat near the centre of a seaside town this was obviously impractical, but at the age of eleven, through a chance meeting of my mother with an old friend who ran a riding school, riding lessons became a reality. The stables were an array of wooden buildings which housed the most wonderful sight I'd ever seen. Ponies of all shapes, sizes and colours stood tied inside these wooden sheds, or outside under a canopy of trees, while children of differing ages groomed and put saddles and bridles on them or simply stood and stroked them. I thought I would burst with happiness. The air was full of chatter and the warm smell of ponies. A small round brown pony was pointed out to me.

"This is Gypsy and she'll look after you for your first ride."

That day was the start of something wonderful. I was allowed to go every Saturday morning and once I became more competent, I helped out in the stables and rode the more difficult ponies.

All my school life I knew I must work with horses or farm, and felt thwarted when my parents decided I should do a secretarial and accounting course before seeking a job, although later in life I thanked them for this decision. It gave me backup and is essential for managing farm accounts. However, on passing my exams I pursued the love of my life and worked in numerous equestrian establishments all over the country, some good and some not so good.

Finally, happily situated in Gloucestershire, I gave a little more thought to my dream of farming, deciding the only option was to marry a wealthy farmer! This of course didn't materialise as I met and fell in love with a young man with great ambition and little finance.

Ours was a chance meeting. My boyfriend of the time was telling me about a motorbike scramble he'd been to, where his friend Aubrey had won. Spontaneously I said I'd love to ride a scramble bike, so this was arranged. Aubrey proudly appeared with this huge lump of shiny metal and, handing me a spare helmet, invited me to ride in front of him round a large field. After giving many instructions he was slightly taken aback by the speed with which I took off, throwing him backwards so all I could see alongside me were two legs in the air.

Recovering his balance, he leant forward and eased my hand off the throttle. Two circuits of the field sufficed for the experience. I climbed off the bike elated, although fully aware that I hadn't really been in control. Aubrey pulled off his helmet as I thanked him, a broad grin spreading across his face. I took in his expression, his shoulder length brown hair and his laughing blue eyes. I was smitten. It was love at first sight.

Besides sheep, Aubrey's other great love was speed: usually on a motorbike. While his main source of fun was scrambling on the steep hills and valleys of local farmland, a road bike was his form of transport to and from town where he was an engineering apprentice. This road bike was nearly the death of him when a car, pulling out of a junction, didn't see him on the main road, as many car drivers fail to see motorbikes, and he was catapulted through the air into the path of another vehicle.

Luckily, he escaped with his life, although sufficiently damaged for his mother to insist he had a lift to town in future.

Still the urge for speed was satisfied by the motorbike scrambling which Aubrey, his friends and cousins were able to do on the hills at Syde. None of them could afford proper scramble bikes so old road bikes were transformed, with knobbly tyres fitted, to enable them to scream up and down the banks quite competitively. He was also quite competitive at motorcycle football. Only a few weeks after I met him and had the exhilarating ride on his bike, I received an unexpected invitation during an evening at the local pub.

"We're doing a display at Chippenham carnival on Saturday," Aubrey announced, as he brought our drinks to the table.

"What, football?" I asked.

"Yeah. You'll come won't you?"

"You bet." I smiled. I'd heard quite a lot about the motorcycle football team, but had yet to see them in action. I wasn't sure whether to get excited or feel apprehensive, but I was certainly going to be there. The last time Aub came back from a display he was covered in bruises and grazes.

I arranged a day off so was able to go with him on the beautiful Saturday in September. The air seemed full of excitement as we neared Chippenham. The whole town appeared to be in carnival spirit and celebrating the fact the late summer weather was warm and dry, the afternoon sunshine and temperature conducive with sleeveless T shirts and shorts.

I'd quickly realised my usual garb of jeans and wellies was something that appealed to Aubrey. He'd never been short of girlfriends, but once he realised the closest they came to owning wellies was a pair of fashion boots that must be kept clean, and lacked any desire to get their hands dirty, these alliances dissolved rapidly. He knew any serious relationship must be with a girl prepared to share his farming dream, as I was.

But that afternoon I'd pulled on a short white skirt and a violet T shirt, which when I glanced in the mirror seemed to go well with my light brown hair and lightly suntanned skin. I smiled as I took in the flags and bunting, pointing out to Aubrey a small pink balloon heading skywards much to the distress of a little girl, trying to persuade her father to catch it. We drove in past the hoopla stands, where long suffering goldfish in plastic bags were waiting to change homes and soft cuddly toys looked almost impossible to win. Laughter and stall holder's shouts mingled with the loudspeakers announcing the Fancy Dress class just about to start in the main ring. As we headed to the left of the field, directed by the steward, we were guided by the roar of motorbike engines being revved up, some just to show off, others, more elderly, to prove they could be stirred into life.

"Looks like we're over there," said Aubrey, driving over to a motley collection of bikes and being greeted by his friends, all from farming backgrounds. I knew several of them, but many others eyed me up and down in approval, Aub suddenly becoming quite proprietary.

Soon the area became a hive of activity. The spectators began to gather and Aub unloaded his bike and kicked it into action, joining the stream of other noises. I looked around, feeling slightly surplus to requirements at that moment, but hovered close-by, knowing Aub would soon want something handed to him. If it was clothing, I could manage. Spanners and wrenches had to be explained a bit and sizes quoted, but I felt I was learning fast.

Aubrey's team was, for some obscure reason, called the Tunnerley Treacle Mines. I had asked him why, but his answer was vague. It was something to do with Big Frank who'd set up the team. I thought it a wonderful name. Big Frank was exactly as described: in his mid forties, tall and well muscled. He was goalie and would later be astride his enormous 4 stroke bike, terrifying the opposition if they dared to approach his goal.

The opposing team could be seen and heard getting ready under another group of trees. Dressed in Royal blue jerseys, they would stand out against the Treacle mine's red and black stripes with yellow numbers on their backs. I was ready to pass Aub his jersey when needed.

"Got anything to drink?" he asked, wiping his grimy hands on a rag. He looked delighted when I produced an old squash bottle I'd filled with diluted orange squash and ice cubes. Aubrey took a long swig.

"That's good," he said. "I should bring you more often." He smiled at me and I beamed back.

The air was thick with bike fumes as riders revved up their machines, and the crowd cheered and waited at the arena.

The game began. The sounds of engines, smell of smoke and oil and shouts of players to each other all mingled into one. The speed at which the ball could travel the length of the pitch, hotly pursued by a man on a motorbike was incredible. A combination of mud and dust flew through the air. There was a roar from the Treacle Mines as they scored a goal. The crowd loved it. Machines crashed with machines and riders seemed to escape serious injury miraculously.

At half-time the exit to the pits opened up rather as I imagined the Red Sea must have done, and I raced after the team, back to their shady spot under the trees. Adrenaline was running high. Aubrey was trying to wipe the dust from his eyes, laughing and shouting to other team members. I rummaged in the car and finding the now less iced squash handed it to him. He smiled, but continued his conversation with Terry, another of the bikers, just wiping his mouth with the back of his hand and smiling at me again as he finished.

"We must be on again in a minute," he said. "That was some first half. They're nearly as good as us. If we hadn't had Frank in goal they might have scored."

"It looks awfully dangerous," I said. I'd been aware of at least one member of the opposing team actually being ridden over during the game.

"Nah, looks far worse than it really is. That's why the crowd love it. They think we'll kill someone, but we try not to." Aubrey laughed.

The second half was as much turmoil as the first, again with riders and bikes coming under the wheels of the opposing team when they failed to move quickly enough. Eventually the Treacle Mines were hailed as winners, by just the one goal of the match, something Aub raved about on the homeward journey.

"First time we've met a team as good as them. They were great. Makes it more of a challenge when we don't just walk over them as usual. We're all meeting at the Chalice tonight. You up for it?" he asked.

Chapter Three

Married Bliss

We were married on a warm, sunny day the following July. Aiming for a small family wedding, my mother was horrified when she discovered the size of Aubrey's family, ours being small and contained. Quite early in our relationship I'd realised that Aubrey was related to most of Gloucestershire and quite a lot of Lancashire. His grandparents had moved down from the North of England during the depression of the 30s when farming looked a lot better on the Cotswolds. And there were a lot of them.

"If you're inviting Georgina and Eric, you'll need to invite Peter and his family and Graham and his family because they are all cousins alike," assured my mother-in-law to be in a very matter of fact way as we sat down to tea.

"Who's Peter?" I asked Aubrey quietly when his Mum left the room to top up the teapot, not having come across Peter yet. Aub shrugged his shoulders; either he had no idea which relative this was, or couldn't remember.

My poor mother nearly had a fit when she saw the length of the guest list. My parents now lived in a small, two-bedroom bungalow where the wedding reception was to be held. Its saving grace was being set in a fairly large garden. This would be a lovely extension to the house for an overflow of wedding guests, but the weather had been bad and so far there had not been a fine Saturday that year.

Marquees for receptions were not the norm then and the cost would have been beyond them anyway. However, my mother's prayers were answered and the day dawned fair, the sun shining, making the whole event less stressful.

The little village church was a picture, decorated by my mother and friends in the choir, who also sang their hearts out during the service. Friends and family all enjoyed the casual layout in the garden and Mum excelled herself with a wonderful finger buffet, all home cooked.

Money was short, as was our honeymoon, simply one night in Sussex. But we'd now rented a little stone cottage in Miserden, a Cotswold village near Birdlip and were pleased to return there. The accommodation was sufficient. We only had a tiny kitchen on one side of a minute hallway, with an equally small bathroom opposite, but the cottage was sat on a sloping bank, and the view from the little sitting room and bedroom window was immense.

The sweeping slopes of Cotswold hills fell away in front on the cottage and the undulating grassland in the distance seemed to go on forever. We were sadly both working in town now, as while Aubrey finished his apprenticeship, I left my job with horses and took an office job, necessary to finance us until Aub qualified and earned more money. Having both come from homes with cats and dogs we also really missed having a pet, so when we were offered a very attractive tortoiseshell kitten with a white tummy, we couldn't resist her.

"She's so pretty," I said, smiling at Aub when he brought the little kitten home. "I love her."

I can't remember what we originally called her, but she soon became Womble, and was a most affectionate cat, greeting us with delight when we returned home from work, rubbing round our legs, then securing a position on a lap for the evening. Of course, soon after Womble had settled in we felt guilty leaving her alone all day, so a very handsome tabby kitten, secured from a local farm, Boogles, joined the family and they adored each other. I'm sure these cats started life with sensible names, but they ended up with silly ones!

The pair would eat together, sleep together, wash each other and stayed close as though joined at the hip. Then came the night when Womble decided to climb the young fir tree precariously growing on a small bank outside our cottage. It was a cold, dark night in early December when the wind was howling and rain driving across in sheets. The tree was swaying from one dangerous angle to another with Womble perched in the top branches rather like the fairy on a Christmas tree.

"How am I expected to get her down?" asked Aubrey quite irately, after gaining no response by calling to her and offering food.

"You'll have to climb up and rescue her," I said. "It's such an awful night we can't leave her there." Womble meowed soulfully.

"What if I fall out of the tree?" Aub asked indignantly as he donned full waterproof clothing and, gritting his teeth, stepped outside into the rain. With much difficulty, as there were few hand or foot holds, he clambered up the spindly pine as far as he could. Amazingly, as the wind swayed the tree even more with Aub's weight on the thin trunk, Womble jumped, or fell, at my feet none the worse for her adventure, although Aub was not quite so unscathed and certainly not in a very good frame of mind. The fact that she was found in the same elevated position the following evening did not arouse any attempt to help her.

When Aubrey qualified as an agricultural engineer, he sensibly accepted a job with the company where he'd trained. This wasn't what he really wanted to do, but he decided this offer was a good move, although he would listen out for a suitable farm job locally as soon as possible. The positive side for me was that this gave me the opportunity to work with horses again as Aub was now being paid a reasonable wage.

Laura was an interior designer living a few miles away. She'd ridden all her life, but now wanted to concentrate on the design company she'd built up, so needed help with the family's horses and ponies. I was delighted to find that Hector, an event horse their elder son had competed on before he disappeared to university, would be available for me to ride.

This new-found job instigated the idea that we could now have a dog. Having fallen for our friends Bearded Collie, Dougal, we'd set our hearts on one, but sadly Beardies were expensive to buy, so when we saw an advert for a one year old dog needing a new home we jumped at the chance. Experience now tells me an advert like that means his previous owners have reached the end of their tether, but at that point we were very naïve!

We trundled off towards Tewkesbury one dark November night, two years after the famous cat rescue, clutching £15 which should have paid the electricity bill. We'd decided if we liked him and if the owners would take £15 (they were asking £20), he could be Aubrey's 21st birthday present.

"This looks like the place," Aub said.

We parked outside an impressive Cotswold stone house, the outside light guiding us up the path. We were shown into a very smart sitting room with a scarlet carpet and white leather furniture by a tall, elegant woman, who said she'd just go and get Florrie. A few minutes later we were greeted by two lovely slate and white beardies of similar type to Dougal who sedately offered greetings and made us welcome.

"Gosh, they're nice aren't they?" I said to Aubrey.

Then it happened.

As if fired from a cannon this mass of light grey fluff launched itself at us. Over the settee where we were seated, and back again. A quick kiss and 'Howdoyoudo?', before leaping over the armchair, then back onto the settee where I was totally flattened. Aub by this point had stood up and was taking refuge by the other chair.

"Oh you've met him," was the understatement, as his breeder re-joined us. "He's so friendly isn't he? He loves people, children and other dogs."

His previous owners had lived on a housing estate and lacking room had kept him in the garage. Unable to give him sufficient care and exercise they'd asked his breeder to find him a good home, preferably in the country.

Aubrey thought he was gorgeous. I heard him say we would definitely have him if she'd take £15 for him, which was accepted. Deep down a nagging voice suggested that paying the electricity bill might have been a more sensible choice, but hey ho, it was his present.

Loaded in our tiny Mini, Florrie sat at my feet, wearing his collar and lead, with a large bowl with DOG on it and the rug he slept on. Ringing in our ears as we drove away was the warning, "Keep hold of him. He sometimes likes to play with the pedals."

Two minutes later Florrie was sitting on my lap. After five

miles of us both huffing and panting, Aub suggested I opened the window a bit to give him some fresh air. It was about 11.15pm, just as we were driving through the middle of Tewkesbury, when Florrie suddenly decided he'd been kidnapped and the small mini window was his line of escape.

In two seconds he'd pushed the window back far enough to enable the front half of his body to emerge from the car like some prehistoric monster. I grabbed his collar, while Aub, very nearly removing a traffic bollard, grabbed at his back legs. Luckily there was very little traffic around and somehow we all escaped unscathed, car and all.

Florrie had no more air until we got home. It was there, in a totally strange village at midnight in the pitch black, that Florrie disappeared. As we unloaded he quite neatly pulled back and left me holding a collar and lead.

"What d'ya mean you've lost him?"

"I didn't. He just walked out of his collar," I said.

Imagine the problem. Trying to call a lost dog as quietly as possible so as not to wake the entire village. Peering into the black, murky night we were both so upset and worried that it was a great relief when, after a couple of minutes he sauntered back, thinking it was now time for bed.

I led him into the house, securely shutting the front door. As I let him go into the sitting room he took one enormous leap onto the settee where both cats had been sleeping. By the time we reached him the cats had fled up the curtains and taken refuge on the pelmets.

It was all too much. We collapsed in giggles like a couple of school kids while Florrie pranced around on his hind legs beneath the curtains and the cats swore at him. The cats slept with us that night as all three were obviously not going to hit it off immediately, and having spent half the night with Florrie didn't want to spend the remainder with him. Luckily in the coming days all three became good friends, although Boogles was always the one in charge.

Chapter Four
Througham and Satan

The following spring Aub was offered a new job, working on a sheep and arable farm close by.

This came with the usual tied accommodation of farming jobs, but the house was an imposing building surrounded by a wild garden high on the top of the Cotswolds.

Here we were exposed to all weathers during the majority of the year, but on a warm sunny day with a light breeze (for there was always wind of some strength), we were enveloped by the songs of skylarks.

There is no need for anyone to pass through Througham unless visiting. The hamlet is a loop off the main road which takes those sufficiently interested to look, past several cottages and farms before re-joining the main road to Stroud. Set on the west facing side of a valley, several of the houses (including Windmill Cottage our new home) have spectacular views over a patchwork of agricultural land. Others nestle deeper in the village. There are two farms, an old Manor house and an Arab stud, with a scattering of farm workers cottages mingled within.

Lower Througham was a working farm, destined to earn an income from its agricultural activities, unlike its neighbour. Donald, the manager, a sometimes surly Scotsman, farmed right through the valley from Througham to Sudgrove and Aubrey was to be responsible for much of the arable and sheep work.

Upper Througham, close by, was owned by playboy Richard, whose finances meant the farm was a hobby to him, which he thoroughly enjoyed, as did Wilf and Mike who worked for him. There were big toys in the form of the latest four-wheel-drive tractors, the livestock was decorative and all three young men had great fun running the place. They also provided us with immense entertainment.

I remember the day I watched Mike in the field opposite our house, testing the electric fence used for strip grazing lambs on turnips. It was a very wet morning when housework looked preferable to doing anything that wasn't essential outside. Having decided to strip the bed and change the sheets I was sidetracked and, looking out of the bedroom window, caught sight of Mike bending down, one hand on the electric fence, the other on the wet ground. Proof that the fence was working showed by the way his glasses kept jumping up and down on his nose as he struggled to let go of the live wire.

I nearly cried with laughter and had to relate the story to Aub when he came home. We weren't sure who knew less about farming, Mike or me, but I was at least becoming aware of some of the basics.

Windmill Cottage had originally been two farm cottages and an outhouse, but had been turned into one without any great imagination. The downstairs walls had simply been knocked through to allow access from one building to the other. This left a fair sized kitchen and dining room on the one side, and an enormous sitting room on the other. Large draughty windows meant the whole house required a huge amount of heating. Fortunately there was an old Rayburn in the kitchen and useful fireplaces in both the dining and sitting room. Although the farm wage was less than Aubrey's previous job, with no rent to pay there was still a little left over to build up the sheep fund, a priority in Aubrey's mind. The other saving grace was the huge stack of free wood we were able to accumulate for the winter.

The outer appearance was sadly not that of a Cotswold stone cottage; more cement covered stone, at one time painted cream. It was due some re-decoration, both inside and out, but it was a wonderful, large house, on the edge of the hamlet with fantastic views of the countryside. It also came with a small paddock, in need of some new fencing, but offering a possibility later to keep a few sheep – or so I was informed once my in-laws had visited our new abode.

They mentioned to other family members that we had this huge garden and a paddock, and soon we were approached by Aubrey's Uncle John with the offer of Satan.

I felt it all started with Satan, although we had already accumulated the two cats, Florrie and several Muscovy ducks. I suppose Satan was the beginning of our farm, at least as far as Aubrey was concerned. He was certainly the beginning of our nightmares.

This was why, one afternoon in early summer, with a cool breeze scuttling the small, infrequent clouds through a silky blue sky, we were standing in Uncle John's garden surveying this superb specimen of a black Welsh Mountain ram. (I was to learn later that he had already been passed around most of the family, but at present we were unsuspecting newcomers.)

"He's absolutely fine, but he does just frighten the children sometimes, so I think it's time he found a new home," John explained.

At the time he had two young children under the age of five and as Satan either ran free range in their garden or on the end of a chain I could appreciate the problem. (Apparently Satan had originally been christened Clive Lloyd after a former West Indies cricketer. The deterioration of his name should have alerted alarm bells, but no, we agreed he could come home with us).

Our transport at the time was an elderly mini countryman, but this allowed Satan sufficient room to travel with the back seats folded down. When introduced to the vehicle Satan hopped in quite agilely, as though he often went out for the afternoon. He came with a little rope halter, so Aub tied him to the back hinge of the mini.

"Just mind his horns," said Uncle John as we left, this message echoing in my ears. "He can be a bit playful."

Our passenger certainly lacked any manners. During the twenty minute drive home he tried to demolish the back end of the mini with his horns and relieved himself in both directions over the interior, shooting lots of little black marbles all over the back of my seat and into the door pocket.

Satan was installed in the back garden on a long chain. He was used to this, although we changed the rope halter for a strong leather collar as the halter was beginning to rub his face. We had to remember not to leave him within view of the front garden on bread delivery days as the baker's girl refused to enter the garden if she could see him. Consequently, on rainy days, the bread was not terribly palatable having spent the day on the garden wall rather than in the bread bin in the porch, although this was soon rectified by leaving the bread bin outside the gate. Our cottage was far too remote to worry about anyone stealing either the bread or the bin.

The other problem with tethering Satan was that almost every day he had to be moved from one tethering position to another. This was not always because he'd eaten all the available grass in that area. If he was annoyed in any way he'd gallop round and round on his tether and mutilate the grass to such a degree that nothing would induce him to eat it. If we forgot or he decided we were being a little slack with the sheep management, he would stand by his tether and 'baa' non-stop in a soul-destroying voice as though explaining to the world he'd been left to starve. Aubrey and I were both working full time, so moving Satan was not our main priority; something he was slow to understand.

And the move was an art of its own. Definitely a two person operation, as the tether peg had to be yanked out of the ground with bionic strength then re-secured with a mallet. This was obviously Aubreys's part of the proceedings. My part was to hold Satan by his horns at the full length of his chain, so he couldn't knock me over.

This was fairly easy because Aubrey caught him first, pulled him to the full extent of his chain, and then handed him to me. As Aubrey pulled out the peg and moved it, all I had to do was keep the chain taut and move Satan at the same time, holding on to him until the peg was firmly anchored again. The awkward part was letting go. The art was to pull him forward as far as he could come, then let go of both horns at the same time, and run. I didn't always escape unscathed. If he could possibly turn his head quickly to catch me with one horn he would.

Not long after he arrived, Satan decided that we obviously had no intention of introducing him to the neighbours, so he would have to make the first move himself.

Our closest neighbours, about a quarter of a mile along the lane, were a couple a little older than us with two young children. Formerly a high flyer in the city, Norman had decided that London was no place to bring up his children, so they had moved to the country.

Norman still had a greater understanding of city life than the countryside, and we were soon to discover he had no great liking for animals. Now simply doing a daily commute to Gloucester, he was happy to return home to a contented wife and two happy children in their new found bliss of country living. All he really wanted at weekends was to dig the garden, have a drink at the pub and play cricket for the local team. Like so many townsfolk, he considered farms were very nice to look at from a distance, and farm animals, in their place, were not objectionable. He wasn't all that keen on mud and droppings left on the public highway to dirty his car, and night time visitations from strange animals were certainly not what he had bargained on.

About ten o'clock the ritual of checking Satan and last minute run for Florrie came into play. For some reason I was in my outside attire before Aubrey, so I was the one who went tentatively into the front garden where Satan was tethered, economising on petrol for the lawnmower. The only trouble was that he wasn't there.

His chain was still there but the U clip which attached it to his collar had come unfastened. I shouted to Aubrey and wandered round the garden calling Satan. It did occur to me that locating a black sheep on a dark night wasn't going to be easy, but lo and behold his grating voice answered from the lane.

"There he is!" I shouted, and rushed up the garden path, out of the gate, grabbed his collar and led him back to his chain triumphantly for Aubrey to secure him. (To begin with I was actually quite brave with Satan). Just then headlights showed coming along the lane.

"Cor, we were just in time rescuing him, weren't we," I said to Aubrey. "He could have been run over or caused an accident."

While Aubrey agreed, the car slowed up as it reached the house and we recognised it and the driver, Norman. He seemed pleased to see us standing there, floodlit by the outside light, holding Satan.

"You've got him then," Norman wound the window down and said in very relieved tones. "I went out to lock the car up and he jumped out from behind the cabbages. I had to run and jump in the car."

Norman explained he hadn't really known what to do, not being sure if Satan was still around, so after sitting in the car for a few minutes he'd decided he would drive along and tell us Satan was loose.

"Oh you needn't have worried," said Aubrey. "You must have frightened him 'cause he's just come home."

"Frightened him!" Norman was dumbfounded after his experience.

He refused our offer of coffee or something stronger to sooth his nerves, pointing out he'd have to come past Satan at close quarters to come inside and he had no intention of doing that.

On inspection the following morning we were rather embarrassed to discover that Satan had taken a bite out of nearly all Norman's cabbages. Just the one bite. He obviously hadn't found one he liked! Until we had fenced the paddock properly Satan was stuck on his chain, as an unchained Satan, loose in a badly fenced paddock was obviously going to be even more of a hazard. Aubrey decided he must get a bigger, stronger U clip, as the present one did look as though it could come apart quite easily. Needless to say, before he got round to getting a new clip, the boy was off again.

Our next alarm call came about quarter to six one morning. Luckily Florrie would always tell us if anyone was about, as with our bedroom at the back of the cottage it could be difficult to hear someone knock at the door. On this occasion, however, I think Richard would have made sure he woke us up. Richard farmed just along the road, although 'farmed' must be said in the loosest of terms. With an executive post in London and worldwide with his father's large business enterprise, he had an excellent social life with money to enjoy, and his farm was his stress relief. Returning home after what, judging by his appearance, had been a rather hectic night, he had been greeted by Satan trotting along the lane to meet him.

"Be two minutes Richard, we'll meet you at your yard."

We donned outdoor gear at speed, gathered up a bucket of nuts and a rope to secure Satan and drove down the hill to Richard's farmhouse. I drove, a fact I was reminded of a little later, because I was obviously the one who parked the car, alongside, but just a little further back from Richard's land rover as he suggested that we should use that to capture and transport Satan. We all climbed into the land rover, which Richard slammed into reverse and swung round, straight into the front wing and light of our mini.

"Didn't see it," he swore. "Didn't know you'd parked it there."

We'd only two minutes previously drawn up before his very eyes and got out of it.

He was most apologetic and said we must send him the bill

for the repairs. Sadly it was obvious to both Aubrey and me that the damage was going to cost more than the car had. Anyway, how could you send a bill to someone who was helping you to capture your animal that was on the loose, probably raiding dustbins and, if we didn't hurry up and catch him, terrorising the entire village.

"Stupid place for Sue to park it," apologised my supportive husband. Under my breath I blamed Richard's obviously failing eyesight, due no doubt to the previous evening's consumption. We disentangled the land rover from the remains of the mini and shot out of the yard at an amazing speed.

It didn't take long to locate the offender. He was quietly nibbling at the contents of one of the dustbins on the bottom road. He raised his head and baa'd when he saw us, looking inquisitively at Richard as if to say "What d'you bring him for?"

As we let the back of the land rover down, Aubrey put a rope round Satan's neck.

"How are we going to get him in?" I asked, as there was quite a gap between the back of the land rover and the road, and by this time Richard had really lost interest in the proceedings.

Satan solved the problem by appearing to say, "Ah you've brought the carriage, good show" and jumped straight in, sitting down on a cushion I hastily removed from under him. He was certainly proving he was a well seasoned traveller.

We took him home in style, secured him in the garden and returned to collect what was left of the mini. Luckily it was quite drivable. In fact it continued to be used with a crumpled wing and the light hanging out for the rest of its useful life. It was later dragged into the garden, stripped of all bits and pieces that stood even a remote chance of being useful for future transport, before joining previous vehicles on Fred's scrap heap. While the mini was in a position on its side, being stripped down, Mrs Emmett, the owner of the Arab stud in the village drove past, giving her groom, Mary a lift to Stroud.

"Oh do look, Mary," she said. "Aubrey and Sue are making another chicken house. How quaint."

This showed the sort of reputation we were beginning to acquire.

Chapter Five

Fred's Musical Evening

Aubrey and I gradually built up friendships with almost all the inhabitants of Througham, although there were one or two with weekend retreats who were there so infrequently it was difficult to get to know them.

Fred and his family were not in this category. Not only did Fred have the adjacent farm, but he also considered himself to be the Lord of the Manor. Not in a flashy, well dressed sense. Simply that he was in charge. Nor was his farm a model of modern agriculture. We soon discovered most of his farming income came from tenants and scrap, the latter which he accumulated in small mountains, virtually out of sight of the road, but you could always tell when he'd been rummaging through a new delivery by the colour of his hands. In the winter it was amusing to see him wearing black fingerless gloves, with matching black fingers.

Fred was the first person to welcome us to the village, as he called it. Technically as it did not have a church, pub or village shop, I thought of it as a hamlet, but that was by the by.

We'd barely unpacked when Fred first made his presence known by parking his battered old white pickup truck outside the gate, blocking the thoroughfare.

"Aub," I called from the kitchen, as I peered out of the

window. "I think we've got a tramp in the garden. Quick, do something."

Although it was a warm spring day, I saw this stocky figure, dressed in a thick black coat which almost reached the floor, with wellington boots protruding beneath, walking down the garden path.

Aubrey joined me looking out of the window and laughed.

"Oh, it's just Fred. He farms along the road," he said. "Donald said he'd probably call and introduce himself."

Aub went to open the door to welcome Fred in, while I still looked out of the window in amazement as our visitor untied and retied the old piece of baler twine around his waist, which was obviously acting as a belt, although not very successfully keeping his coat in place. The coat had probably originated in an army and navy stores, although it may have passed to Fred via a jumble sale. Originally made for someone far taller, it partially concealed his black wellies and extended past his wrists. A black woollen hat was pulled well down over his ears although a fair amount of grey hair could still be seen, sticking out at odd angles.

I decided to go out and meet him, not wanting him in my house. Meeting on the garden path seemed to suit Fred, although we were later to find if he wanted to come into the house he would! However, today he was more interested in what we might be going to do with the garden, especially with the old stable at the far end, where we were intending to make the majority of the grassed piece into a small paddock.

"Gonna keep an 'orse then are you?" he said, in more of a statement than a question.

Aubrey laughed. "I'm hoping to make this secure for Satan and we did think we might have a few chickens or something."

Fred nodded his head, sagely. "Them's always useful, although I produce fresh eggs at the farm. You'm must come along and see us. Elizabeth would be glad to see another female around." He nodded at me.

By the time another vehicle wanted to pass along the road, we'd learnt about his long suffering wife Elizabeth, who would always have the kettle on should we be able to pop in when passing, and his two sons, who we were to become great friends with.

"You must come along for a musical evening," was Fred's passing shot as he drove away. "I'll be in touch."

"Well, he's an eye opener," I said, sinking down on the small wooden bench outside the cottage. "Are all the neighbours going to be like him?"

"No idea, but he's quite a case. Not sure I fancy a musical evening."

"Maybe not, but I expect we'll have to go to it. We'll probably meet all the rest of Througham there as well so it could be quite fun."

A week or so later I mentioned our invitation to Joan, Norman's wife, who smiled knowingly. "Ah, you've been invited to one of those, have you? Oh no, we won't be there," she added. "Norman and Fred don't see eye to eye about the cricket team at the moment so they're not speaking, but you'll enjoy it."

We had almost forgotten about the invitation when it did arrive, or summons as Aubrey felt it was. Wilf, Fred's older son, dropped in on his way back from work.

"The old man's expecting you two to his musical evening tonight about sevenish. He's doing supper. He says don't be late."

Although a chilly evening, we decided to walk the half mile along the road to Fred's farm. A little surprised that no cars overtook us, we chatted about who else might be there, but on our arrival saw no cars parked in the yard. Aubrey looked at his watch and decided that as we were in plenty of time, we might be the first there, and suggested we hovered about for a bit, but Elizabeth, who had seen us walking down the lane, opened the front door and called us in.

A tall, well built woman with long hair showing a few grey streaks through the dark brown, her eyes smiling a welcome. "Don't worry about that," she said, dusting off her hands on her floral apron, as I looked around for somewhere to wipe my shoes that had got muddy crossing the yard.

"Shall I take them off?" I suggested.

"Don't be silly, just come straight in."

Neither Aubrey nor I had been in Fred and Elizabeth's house before, but it was very basic. The kitchen had at one time probably been painted a light green, or maybe cream. It was difficult to tell now. An old Welsh dresser (which was so well stacked with papers, magazines and beer mats where one would expect to find plates that it was almost difficult to recognise), stood against one wall, and there was a large wooden table bearing the scars of family life in the centre of the room. A selection of chairs were available, none matching nor even looking as though originally destined for use in a kitchen, and most were accommodating at least one cat.

"Sit ye down. I've just made a brew, but Fred says you'll take some of his wine," Elizabeth informed us.

"Actually I'd love a cup of tea," said Aubrey, not a great wine drinker.

"Nay, you don't want that. I've got some beer for us," said

Fred, coming into the kitchen. "But a nice drop of red for your lady. We'll have the cheese out Elizabeth."

To my amazement Fred was dressed in similar apparel to when we first met, even down to the wellies. I also had to admire his designer stubble. A thoroughly modern man. Later I was to wonder when he did shave, because I never once saw him clean shaven, nor with more than two or three day's growth on his face.

"Is anyone else coming?" I couldn't help asking hopefully.

"Nay, this evening is just for yourselves. We'll move into the music room when we've eaten and you can enjoy that."

Supper consisted of a large hunk of cheddar cheese, a crusty loaf and a dish of butter, all of which were excellent. Elizabeth chatted to me about the village and others who lived there, some of whom we had yet to meet, while Fred quizzed Aubrey on the state of farming at Lower Througham. Every few minutes a cat appeared on the table, mainly at Fred's end where it received a piece of cheese and left. At one point one of the cats ventured towards Elizabeth's end where it was smartly smacked across the backside and shot off the table and out of the room.

"Damned things," she said. "Fred spoils 'em rotten, but I think they ought to know their place." She started to clear away the food as Fred indicated to us that we should move into the music room.

"Bring your glass with you," said Fred, handing me an almost full bottle of home brewed red wine. I'd only sipped a little of what was in my glass, but accepted the bottle with good grace.

"Come on, I've a fire going in here," he said and led the way through, carrying a jug of the home brewed beer I could see Aubrey was struggling to drink.

Fred kicked the remains of a small tree across the carpet, pushing the burning end further into the grate. A small amount of evening light was still attempting to filter in through the grimy window, a soft coat of some type of algae clinging to it determinedly. The walls must definitely have been a greyish green in here at some point, although grey was the predominant colour now, and the smell of damp could not quite be smothered by that of smoke and charred wood, because to call it a fire was a great exaggeration.

Fred indicated for us to sit down, although the variety of chairs were not really inviting. I located a cloth covered one with dirty wooden arms, while Aubrey selected a leather one with a protruding spring until Fred said he couldn't sit there, because it would be painful, and pulled out another leather one in slightly better condition. Fred's own chair was dark red and fairly upright with a warm green rug over the back.

"Is Elizabeth joining us?" I asked, looking towards the kitchen.

"Nay, she isn't really interested in classical music."

I could hear Aubrey thinking neither was he, but he said nothing. Fred took several minutes to set the music going on his old record player, then he sat back in his chair, legs outstretched in front of the fireplace, elbows on the armrests and fingers together as if praying. His eyes gradually closed and the only way we could tell he was awake was from his two index fingers tapping together in time with the music which, although not unpleasant, was not really what we usually listened to.

I finished my glass of wine and poured another one. Aubrey scowled at me. I raised an eyebrow at him. If I had to sit here listening to this, I was jolly well going to drink, even though I'd tasted better wines.

"Would you like some," I offered him the bottle.

"Might as well, I suppose," he whispered. "This is revolting."
He disappeared into the kitchen to empty the rest of his beer
down the sink.

"I think Elizabeth's gone out or gone to bed," he whispered
on his return. "She's certainly not in the kitchen." The record
finished and Fred, immediately alert, leapt to his feet.

"Excellent, excellent. You enjoyed that. Good. Good" and
he changed the record for another, kicked the smouldering tree
a little further into the fireplace and resumed his posture in his
chair. There was obviously to be nothing talked about.

A while later the proceedings were repeated, but this time,
after kicking the tree Fred left the room. No explanation, but I
guessed a visit to the loo must be necessary.

We sat there together, still vaguely listening to the sounds of
Mozart, not reproduced in the best of quality. After ten minutes
or so Aubrey wandered off into the kitchen again, and from the
hallway caught sight of Fred just disappearing up the stairs.

"I think he's gone to bed," Aub said, returning to the sitting
room.

"What? He can't have." I stared at him in disbelief.

"Well they've got a downstairs bathroom and I heard the loo
flush then he disappeared upstairs. I think Elizabeth went up
ages ago."

"This is mad. Are we just meant to go and leave the fire like
this?"

"Well it hasn't looked too enthusiastic all evening, so I doubt
if it's going to spring into life now. Let's just try to get the end of
it into the fireplace, then if it does burn down it won't burn the
carpet." Looking at the well worn remains of a putty coloured

floor covering of sorts, it seemed unlikely that this would fuel an inferno.

We put our glasses and the bottle of wine in the kitchen, and closed the front door. Walking home, we tried very hard to contain our laughter until we were out of earshot. It was an evening we were going to remember for a long time.

Chapter Six

Spring Lambing

Aubrey's move to Lower Througham coincided with lambing. He was looking after a flock of six hundred Scotch Halfbred ewes, a cross between Border Leicesters and North Country Cheviots, favoured by Donald with his Scottish ancestry. He'd worked with this type of sheep for years and these ewes ran with Suffolk rams to produce meat lambs. They were bigger and heavier sheep than Aubrey had come across before, but well adjusted to the climate on the escarpment, excellent mothers and they produced good quality lambs.

Lambing continues twenty four hours a day and Aub was often the one doing most of the night shifts, but it never worried him. I would ensure he had sandwiches and cake to go with his flask of tea, and there was an old caravan in the sheep shed where he could keep warm if there was a lull in proceedings.

Most evenings when I returned from work I would take supplies down to him and spend a couple of hours in the shed gaining as much knowledge as possible about sheep, well aware of my ignorance.

"Hi Gorgeous," Aubrey shouted as he appeared at the sheep shed entrance, smiling at the sight of me approaching with my tousled hair sticking out beneath a sensible woollen hat. He took in my waterproof clothing and appreciated that I'd come to stay a while.

"Come and have a look at these," he said, having wrapped his arms around me and kissed me. "I'll give you some problem solving this evening."

He led the way towards a line of pens each with a ewe and three lambs.

"Right. We don't leave any of the ewes with three lambs; it isn't fair to them as they've only got two teats and, although they may be producing enough milk for three at the moment, they won't cope later on. I'm taking one off and putting it with the other cade lambs over there until we have a ewe that has a single and we adopt a second lamb onto her. Now, which lamb am I going to take off?" he asked, looking at me.

I studied the ewe and her lambs, which were all lying down in a corner looking very contented.

"Do you know if she has any preference for any of them?" I asked tentatively, thinking how awful it must be to have three babies one minute, and then find you'd lost one.

"Oh dear, I can see this is going to be painful." Aub pulled a face. "Come on, you have to be sensible in farming. Unless I've seen her truly disliking one, that doesn't come into it. Look at them though. Those two are slightly smaller than this one. If I leave him and a smaller one he'll soon scoff all the milk and we'll have a screwy little one alongside him, so he's the one coming out." And he lifted the bigger lamb gently from the pen and carried it across the shed to the cade lamb pen. Putting it down on the fresh straw the lamb stretched, looked around and soon settled down again with the other four lambs in the pen under the warm heat lamp.

"Won't his mother miss him?" I asked, amazed at how easy it had been to remove the lamb.

"Not really. He didn't even call to her, but if they do they're far enough away from the lambing pens for the mother not to really be aware of it. Now is a good time to move them as they are full and content. I probably won't even try to bottle him until the morning when he'll be really hungry and should suck a teat easily. Tomorrow the ewe will go out in the paddock with her two lambs and they become a unit and she'll be quite happy. Right, which one is coming out of this pen?"

I immediately picked the larger lamb, but as he was suckling Aubrey said he'd leave them for the moment until it was full and settled down.

At other pens of triplets, the lambs were all of a similar size, so any could be taken, but at the end of the row of pens an old ewe was struggling with two lambs, one of which was far smaller and weaker than its mate.

"She probably started off with three and one has been re-absorbed, so the little one is a smaller triplet and I think it's going to struggle with its big brother."

"Why are they so different in size?"

"A ewe carries lambs in two horns of its womb, and having three, she will have carried two on the one side. The smaller lamb is the survivor from that side, but initially it will have been sharing sustenance with another until she re-absorbed it."

"Why would it re-absorb, that's early abortion isn't it?"

"Yeah. Something could have been wrong with it. She's an old girl and may not have had enough condition on her to maintain three. Nature's quite incredible when it knows what the animals can cope with. Her body can re-absorb to boost her. This little one's just managing to get in and have a suck when its big brother has finished. It's got a full tummy." Aubrey picked up the lamb by its front legs allowing the body to hang down. "You can see best this way if they're full or not. I think I'll still take the bigger one off because she's looking after this little one so well, and motherly love will keep it going better than me bottling it. Little ones like this are difficult to adopt onto another ewe because if the ewe isn't keen to take it, the lamb can lose the will to live, whereas with big strong people, like this one…" He picked up the bigger lamb. "They only think of their stomachs, so they'll be happy even if we have to tie the adopting ewe up."

Quietly, without any fuss he carried the bigger lamb over to the others to be bottled. It baa'd, annoyed at having been moved, but its mother was still nuzzling her smaller lamb.

Aub said, "The old girl may well stay in a couple more days. I'll move her into the far barn tomorrow, but a couple more days inside will strengthen both her and her lamb. I always keep slightly dodgy ones separate from the main flock."

I took it all in with great admiration. Aub's compassion for the animals and the way he worked both night and day. But none of it was anything other than a way of life for him. I followed him through to the main barn where the ewes still to lamb were checked regularly.

"There's one on over here." Aubrey quietly climbed the hurdle gate into the barn and quickly caught the ewe. He bent her head round to the side and toppled her over onto her side, legs towards him, holding her down with his knee on her neck. "Here, you can hold this ewe for me," he suggested. I tentatively approached the ewe.

"Kneel down the far side to hold her, then she can't kick you," Aubrey instructed. "She's been struggling a while now; she must have a problem."

He reached for a bucket of water and washed his hands then collected another that held ropes and antiseptic lubricant which he smoothed over his right hand before gently feeling around her backside.

"The lamb's probably got a leg back. I could see a bit of a nose coming. Hopefully it isn't coming just head first. No that's good; I've got one front leg. I just need to push the lamb back so I can get my hand in and find the other one."

With expertise, Aubrey pushed the lamb's shoulders and head back inside the ewe and then traced his way round the shoulder to locate the other front leg.

"She's having two lambs. I can feel two more feet this side of the shoulder so both lambs are trying to come at once but neither is presented correctly," he murmured to me, his mind really on the job in hand. He felt around in the confined space of the birth canal and then smiled.

"This is the right one. You have to be sure the leg you find is connected to the same lamb; otherwise you'll cause all sorts of problems and be totally stuck. Make sure you cup your hand over the foot before you turn it or the little hoof could tear the womb. Here he comes." He had gently manipulated both feet into the correct position and with a hearty push the ewe ejected the first lamb. Aubrey quickly wiped its nose with some clean straw and rubbed its side but it was soon happily breathing and he passed it round to the front to the ewe.

He put his hand back inside the ewe to feel for the second lamb.

"I'll leave her a bit to sort this one out and hopefully she'll lamb the second one herself. I can just feel both feet so it looks like it's coming the right way. Better not to interfere too soon."

We both stood up and admired the new arrival. Aubrey washed his hands and dried them on an old piece of towel hung close by.

"You go back home now, and tell that big hairy dog to look after you." He smiled. "I'll check the others, then come back to see that this one's OK."

"Are you coming home at all tonight?"

"Probably not. Will I see you in the morning?"

I assured him I'd be down with a bacon buttie quite early, knowing Aubrey would be home sometime during the day for a bath and change of clothes when Donald took over his shift.

Chapter Seven

Mary and Friends

Througham was quite a tightly knit community. The cottages scattered along the side of the hill operated a very effective grapevine of news. Fred picked up useful titbits from Wilf, who worked (or rather was employed) at Upper Througham Farm, which stood above Lower Througham Farm in both geographic and social position. From a different source, Aub and I were amused to gather that the repair bill for the machinery Wilf damaged far outweighed any profit that could have been gained from his employment.

Between the two farms lay The Manor and The Court. Both had been built in the heyday of the woollen industry. The Manor was built using the traditional golden Cotswold stone, usually found in the more Northern villages of Moreton in Marsh and Chipping Campden. The Court had obviously had some Italian influence as it was built of cream coloured smooth stone with wonderful topiary in the front garden and magnolia trees in a small courtyard at the back, that could just be seen from the road. Both had imposing stable blocks although it was only the Court's stables that were used. This was where Mrs Emmett and her wonderful Arab horses resided.

Surrounding these two palatial residences was a sprinkling of Cotswold cottages in varying states of upkeep, mainly housing members of the 'arty crafty' set. Proud of their lack of television, they either peddled everywhere on a rusty old bicycle or urged life into some battered old vehicle of the same vintage as ours. There seemed to be no shortage of vegetarians, who gave superb dinner parties and passed on some wonderful recipes to me.

I soon became firm friends with Mary, who lived with husband Max in one of the cottages lower down in the village. They'd both fallen about laughing when I recited the tale of Fred's musical evening.

"Oh goodness, yes he does that to everyone he can rope in. Elizabeth just stands by and lets it happen because she knows there is nothing she can do about it, but you only get caught the once, don't you!" laughed Mary.

"It was hilarious," I agreed, "especially when we discovered Fred and Elizabeth had both gone to bed and left us on our own."

"They always do," said Mary. "I had to go once but Max refused to come so I was left completely on my own."

Mary had quite recently taken on the job of caring for the two Arab stallions and several broodmares at the stud owned by Mrs Emmett, while Max designed electronic dashboards for the latest giant tractors. Based near Stroud, a job with a delightful stone cottage in this locality had been a bonus to them.

A beautiful stable door led into the clean, light kitchen. The walls were painted a warm cream, an old-fashioned black stove provided warmth, surrounded by pale blue cupboards.

"It didn't look this great when we moved in. The original back door came off its hinges, nearly killing Upton." She smiled at the Springer spaniel lying at her feet.

Clutching my mug of tea, I followed Mary through the

cottage, admiring the handmade patchwork furnishings and beautiful watercolours.

"That's Upton isn't it?"

"Yes. I love painting animals."

We wandered back to the kitchen and sat drinking tea.

"It is brilliant, isn't it," I said. "You're lucky having such a view from down here because it's also quite sheltered. Up with us when the wind's blowing it howls a gale. That damn windmill's going to drive us insane."

Windmill Cottage, where we lived, gained its name not from some architecturally designed masterpiece, but from a rusty old iron windmill mentioned on the Ordnance Survey maps, so couldn't be removed. Even in the slightest breeze it clanged and whirled itself into action and although Aubrey had tried his best to wedge it to stop it turning, as it no longer served any purpose, he risked being decapitated if the air moved even slightly while he was up there. In the back of his mind he did have a solution for this, and some months later during spring ploughing accidentally hit the windmill very hard about four times until it fell to the ground.

"We really must introduce you to the others," Mary said. "You and Aubrey must join our supper evenings. We get together with Mike and Linda and Nicky and Joel along the lane quite often. Have you met them? We either take it in turns to do a whole meal or everyone brings a course. Tell you what, we'll try to organise one this weekend. Mike and Linda are vegetarians but I've found some wonderful cheap 'dinner party' options with veg from the garden. Nicky's good with ideas too."

"I haven't met Nicky and Joel yet, though Aubrey may have. He's in the village more than I am."

"They're Aussies. Good fun for an evening. Nicky does a

super tomato bake thing. Max had a bit of a bonus last week so I'll do supper, just bring a few beers. Do you make homemade wine?"

"No. Should we?" I asked.

"It's cheaper than bought stuff. Often tastes revolting but I've got some Max made last year that's quite drinkable. Rhubarb I think. We'll drag a couple of bottles out. A sort of 'welcome to the clan dinner'."

I was really looking forward to becoming more involved with the locals. Working away from Througham I found it harder to integrate than Aubrey did. He seemed to know most in the village already.

"Sounds good," Aubrey said when I told him that Mary had confirmed Saturday evening that week for supper. "I'll get some beers in, but I expect they already make their own. We'd better start producing something. You can get these kits for wine and beer making. Perhaps we should give it a go."

He disappeared off, rifling through some old magazines until he found what he wanted.

"Here it is. Make your own wine, red white or rosé, from a kit. Can you pop into Stroud and get one. It's a Boots advert, get the rosé one. I like rosé."

"I know you do," I sighed. "I always think of rosé as being for indecisive people. Those who don't know if they want red or white," I added cheekily.

"You saying I'm indecisive?"

I just raised my eyebrows and smiling, turned away and continued serving up the supper. I could feel Aub scowling at my back.

The evening at Max and Mary's was the start of a long friendship. As Max worked away from the village, Aub hadn't met him before but they hit it off immediately, although Aub had to admit he could see Max in a definite 60s role of 'cool man'.

All eight of us were lounging around the table in mix and match chairs, painted in beautiful pastel shades, some collected from bedrooms to make up the numbers. Candles and nightlights made the room glow, reflecting on the assorted glassware and crockery. After consuming the delicious meal, the conversation mellowed well. One of the main topics of conversation was Satan. Other members of the party were fairly unanimous about their lack of affection for him.

"I know you say you'd love to have your own flock of sheep but how did you come to have that horned black thing?" asked Joel, not meaning to be rude but he had drunk quite a bit as the evening wore on.

"Hey, that's not a very nice way to describe him. His name is Satan," I said, feeling rather protective towards our ram.

"And a most appropriate name too," agreed Joel. "Is there any more beer chaps?" He raised an eyebrow at Mike.

"He was a gift," Aubrey explained. "I don't think we had any idea what we were taking on but it seemed like a good idea at the time."

There were a few murmurings about situations some of the others had got themselves into that had appeared better at the time than in the cold light of day. Mike produced another jug of homemade beer which seemed to go down well with all but Aubrey, who accepted another half glass of the dwindling rhubarb wine.

"This is quite good Max," said Aub. "I just hope my packet

stuff works as well."

"I mean, you can't produce a flock of sheep with just a ram. Are you going to get some ewes as well?" suggested Joel.

Aub and I looked at each other. I certainly hadn't got that far in my thoughts about Satan, but Aub obviously had.

"Well I'm hoping to, but we haven't got anywhere to keep them at the moment … and a flock of ewes would cost a bit, which we don't have."

"Couldn't you get a couple from Donald? Old throw-outs or something. They might keep Satan away from the dustbins for a bit," said Mike, laughing.

"I'm sure Fred would let you graze the paddock along the road from you," said Linda. "He hasn't got much stock these days and that field doesn't look as though it's been grazed for a while."

The conversation flowed on with suggestions that swayed from practical to most impractical including possible night time sheep rustling, which greatly appealed to Joel who volunteered to help with that. Once the wonderful suggestions ceased, Aubrey agreed that talking to Donald about a couple of older ewes and to Fred about the field would be a good idea.

"I don't think sheep rustling is the way forward but thank you all for the advice," he added laughing, as we left the party. We walked home discussing the possibilities of wives for Satan.

Chapter Nine
Satan's Wives and Family

The following morning Aubrey broached the subject of ewes with Donald who agreed that keeping a ram on a chain was not going to work for long, and running him with a couple of ewes made far more sense. Donald was also well aware how desperately Aubrey wanted some sheep of his own.

"You sort out with ol' Fred about the field and give me a couple of days to think about this," he said, scratching his chin. "Could work out."

Fred was quite happy to rent us the field for a small amount and when we discussed our finances, Aub thought we could probably manage to buy two or three older ewes which might make life a lot better for both us and Satan. It was food for thought. A couple of days later Aub bounced in the door and filled me in with Donald's suggestion.

"Donald knows an elderly lady with four Black Welsh Mountain ewes to sell, but she's more concerned that they'll be well looked after than the price. He was right when he said we ought to keep the same breed if we could, 'cause he thought we might want to sell the whole flock sometime later and buy what he rudely called proper sheep." Aubrey grinned at me.

"The nerve of the man." I smiled back at him. "You mean to say all sheep don't have horns and bad tempers?"

The outcome of this found us late one evening, using a torch and the lights of the shed to assist as much as possible, playing push-me pull-you with four little black ewes.

Small they might be, but even so four ewes were not going to fit into the back of our beaten up old mini, so we'd borrowed a land rover and trailer from Richard, who had definitely expressed his desire to see Satan installed in a field with women to keep his mind off night visits.

The lady owner, who was helpfully shining a light to assist with loading, had agreed a very reasonable price and I was greatly relieved to know we hadn't spent all our savings. More sheep would be an ongoing expense until they produced some lambs and they were ready for sale. After a lot of persuasion, pushing and pulling we eventually got one ewe inside the trailer only to have her try to leave again as we encouraged her friends in, but eventually they were all loaded and we took our little flock home for Satan.

Satan was delighted. They certainly gave him a new lease of life and he rapidly settled down to the job in hand and fairly soon we were happy that all should be in lamb. Satan settled down to guard his flock and seemed pleased with the company. The small field we had been lucky enough to rent was about 100 yards along the lane. A good crop of brambles decorated the roadside stone wall, and during the blackberry season, it was a source of great amusement to see brave but foolish pickers venture into the paddock for the cream of the crop on Satan's side, only to vault back over the gate with an agility that often belied their age and stature, hotly pursued by Satan's charging form.

The following spring the first of our black ewes gave birth to a beautiful black single ewe lamb a little earlier than expected due to Satan's enthusiasm. Coming during the night or early in the morning she'd been a wonderful surprise to see when I got up. Aubrey had checked her late the previous night but she hadn't really looked as though she was going to lamb imminently so he hadn't warned me. Born on Grand National Day, she was christened Velvet.

We'd never named the ewes, mainly because they were quite hard to tell apart. This was an era before individual ear tags were required and as the ewes looked identical it was difficult to determine which was which, until now. I was a little disappointed she'd only had one lamb not twins, or even triplets as the ones at Lower Southam had produced, but Aubrey told me I should be pleased with what we'd got, so I shut up.

"These are hill sheep really so they often won't produce more than one lamb. Mind you, that one looks like she could be carrying two." He pointed to another of the ewes who he thought was going to be a bit later than the rest although she looked a fair size already. Over the next three weeks two of the other ewes produced Leticia, (named after childhood memories of Larry the Lamb's sister in Toytown) and Lucinda, but the climax was the final arrival of Sooty and Sweep, twin ewe lambs from the larger ewe, miraculously bringing the total crop to five females. After consistent watching and ready assistance that wasn't at all necessary, it was lovely to have the complete family and all girls.

We were very proud of our small flock, but not as proud as Satan was. For a while he had to be chained up in the adjoining field as he refused to let anyone enter the ewe's field to check on them and their lambs, especially me.

Every evening when I arrived home from work, I would leave Florrie in the kitchen while I walked along the road to check the sheep, often with the cats strolling along behind me. They would jump up onto the stone wall along the lane and skip along the coping stones like little acrobats; enjoying my company. I felt the ewes and lambs were the sweetest time wasters I'd seen, the little black flock standing out well on the emerald green summer grass, like a Constable landscape.

Later, in June, Aubrey sheared our mighty flock of Satan and the four ewes. One sunny Sunday afternoon the flock was driven into the front garden, Satan secured on his collar and the lambs safely separated into the back garden behind the house out of the way while we concentrated on the job in hand. Aubrey did the catching and shearing and I got to work rolling fleeces. The entire operation took about three hours, a little longer per sheep than his uncle took with the Swales, although the greater proportion of time was taken with setting up the machine and tea breaks rather than actual shearing.

Satan was remarkably easy to shear; sitting back quite relaxed and looked very smart when Aubrey had finished him.

"Hang on a minute; I'll just get the camera. I must have a picture of him looking so dapper," I said, disappearing indoors.

"He's still got a few clipping lines, but he's come out of his wool looking great, hasn't he?" said Aubrey, rather pleased with his handiwork. It was a long time since he'd done much shearing as Donald had arranged for a mob of New Zealanders to do the farms' ewes.

After a little more admiration, Satan was secured on his chain again, out of the way before he could assist with the rest of the proceedings. Throughout the afternoon we were accompanied by Velvet bawling in the back garden that we'd taken her mother away from her, although Leticia, Lucinda and the twins didn't seem at all perturbed. When we eventually finished we decided to turn all the sheep into the back garden as the grass was rather long, but regretted this move all night as Velvet continued to complain that not only had we taken her mother away, in return we'd given her some strange looking wool-less creature who kept following her around. It took her a full twenty-four hours to accept that this was her mother with a new hairstyle.

As the summer progressed Aubrey had more time to play around with scramble bikes during the longer evenings. I would often go across the valley with him and meet up with other couples, the men playing on their bikes and the girls lazing on the sunny banks watching them. There was even talk of competing at another scramble but nothing seemed to materialise. When the men collapsed on the grass with the girls after their strenuous exercise, Aubrey and I lay on our backs, watching the little blobs of cotton wool clouds floating by on the breeze.

"If clouds were sheep we'd have quite a flock," I said to Aub smiling.

Chapter Ten

Dipping

As with Aubrey's uncle's hill sheep, it was important the sheep were dipped later in the summer to avoid getting fly strike, scab and other such antisocial complaints.

Luckily Donald was most amenable about running our sheep through the dip after his had been done, but the dip was situated at the far end of a track beyond Lower Througham farm, meaning quite a trek for the four ewes, five lambs and Satan from their paddock to the next farm. Easier said than done.

As we didn't have a sheepdog, I was often used as one, but today Aubrey, as flock-master, decided I should walk in front of the sheep to direct them while he brought up the rear with the mini. This was to be quite a technical operation as the sheep had to be persuaded to leave their paddock, turn left along the lane past our cottage to the first road junction where I was to turn right waving a bucket of feed and shouting words of encouragement hoping they would all follow me. They were then to go down the hill, right again at the bottom and along to the sheep pens and dip.

"Shall I hope they follow me and the bucket down the hill? Or turn them at the corner?" I asked.

"Well you'd better walk in front with the bucket, hadn't you? Otherwise you'll get left behind and we'll have chaos at the bottom of the hill" said Aubrey.

"Do you think we should ask Mike or Wilf to give us a hand?" I suggested. "What do we do if they don't go the right way?"

"They'll be fine. Stop looking for problems."

So I stood at the paddock gate rattling the nuts in the bucket appetisingly, awaiting some reaction, while Aubrey did his one and only task on foot of shooing the sheep towards me. All seemed to be going according to plan. The flock trotted up to me expectantly and happily followed me as I moved off along the lane. The flock-master closed the gate, stepped into his transport and we all proceeded in an orderly fashion. Suddenly there was a glint in Satan's eyes.

'Oh look, mothers in front of me with no gate between us, and she's got a bucket of nuts. Whoopee!' was what appeared to pass through his warped little mind, I was sure, and in a split second he'd lowered his head and charged.

He flattened both me and the bucket. I scrambled up, a bit battered, brushed myself off, and looked back just in time to see Satan (who had trotted back to his wives just to make sure they'd seen and fully appreciated what he'd done) turn and gather speed towards me again. As he reached me I grabbed his horns. No mean feat when I thought of it, but after being walloped by them once I wasn't aiming to be caught again. The force with which he met me sent both of us to the ground, and I sat on the road clinging to Satan's head, praying that I would be able to hold onto him.

"Aub, help," I shouted. Aubrey leapt out of the car and strode towards me, but instead of gallantly offering any help, simply responded with "What do you think you're doing? You've let all the blasted ewes go past you."

All nine animals had trotted on serenely but they had no intention of turning right down the hill, instead heading straight for the main road.

After a short interval of probably only a minute, during which we poured abuse on each other, Aubrey chained Satan up in the garden as we were right outside the house and we both jumped into the car to head the rest of the sheep off before they reached the main road.

They were retrieved and dipped, including Satan who travelled down in the back of the car, although Aubrey then decided he'd ask Richard if he could borrow the land rover and trailer to get him home as even he couldn't face the car smelling of sheep dip for the next six months.

"Pity you didn't think of that in the first place," I said, nursing my bruises. We didn't say a lot to each other, but I made it quite plain that either Satan went or I did.

Chapter Eleven

Geese

Alternate Sunday afternoons were often spent with Aubrey's parents and any other family members that were around. Invariably, a typical North Country tea was put before us, making us glad Sunday lunch had simply been a sandwich!

Aubrey's mother was the most sociable of people and the easiest way to offend her was to refuse any part of this delicious meal, so we endeavoured not to.

One such Sunday afternoon we'd hardly seated themselves at the table when his mother burst out her news that a neighbour of theirs' had five geese wanting a good home, so she'd told the people that she was sure we'd love to have them.

Aubrey and I looked at each other – geese?

"Why would we want geese, Mum?" asked a mystified Aubrey. "We don't know anything about geese."

Mind you we didn't know much about ducks and they'd survived. All I could remember about the species was attending a riding school where geese had grazed the orchard surrounding the outside loo and the hazard of running there with my friends without the geese seeing us. If the geese then got interested in what we were doing it was possible to end up with six or eight children hiding in the loo, none daring to make their escape back across the orchard.

"They lay very large eggs and they sell for 10 pence each," Aubrey's mum continued, serving large slices of delicious ham onto our plates and offering round a bowl of home grown tomatoes that smelt so appetizing. She was obviously convinced that we'd have these geese. "They don't want anything for the geese and there's a house that goes with them."

This seemed to be the ultimate persuading point in her mind. It also appeared that the present owner had an unlimited supply of stale bread which he would continue to collect for us to feed them. The fact that the geese weren't going to cost us anything began to increase our limited interest.

"Why are they getting rid of them?" asked Aub, becoming a little shrewder after the Satan episode.

"Oh, because they go away a lot, now they're retired and can't get anyone reliable to look after them," replied his mother, adding some hot potatoes to the slices of cold meat on his plate.

"Always off gallivanting on cruises they are these days," said Aubrey's father. "Thought we might look at one sometime," he added dryly to his son as his wife flicked the tea cloth she was holding across his hand.

"Don't talk such rot," she said. "Now would you like some beetroot and some homemade pickles? Let's start then."

This was another of those moments when the little red warning light should have appeared to at least one of us. Why did no one want to look after them when the owners went away?

But no, we fell hook, line and sinker for the offer and before we knew it, we were being hotly pursued around the garden by Gustav the gander, knowing at last full well why others weren't too keen on him.

Gustav and his four wives took up residence in the small

paddock, now fenced, with the ducks, who gave the geese a very wide berth. Two of the wives were quite normal geese, of fair size and proportions and white in colour. The third had only one eye and bore the very original name of Blindy. To see where she was going she had to hold her head on one side with her good eye pointing forwards, which gave her a sort of Cyclops effect. Blindy was the only goose we were able to catch fairly easily, without loss or damage to limbs or eyes, as we could creep up on her blind side and pounce on her.

The fourth wife, Sloopy, was darker than the others, a mixture of greys and white, with deformed wings which meant she looked as though she was trying to take off all the time and meant she took up twice as much space as the others in the goose house.

Initially, all seemed serene. They all lived together quite happily, at nights coming into the shed that had come with them. Then they started laying, followed by the sitting ritual.

"It says here that it's best to take the fertile eggs away from the geese and put them under broody hens as geese are bad mothers," I said, looking in the self-sufficiency book Linda had lent me. I'd been trying quite hard to find out more about goose management.

"But we haven't got any chickens," I pointed out to Aubrey.

"Not yet, but don't let my mother remember that or some will miraculously appear from somewhere."

"Just for once that might be useful according to my book," I laughed. "We'll just have to hope they can incubate them themselves."

One thing we should have thought of was Gustav. Gustav was difficult enough to catch and do anything with anyway, but if we'd thought about it we may have removed him from the goose house when his wives started laying. Of course we didn't.

Once his wives started making nests and incubating the eggs Gustav took it upon himself to stand guard. This meant as soon as I poked my head inside the shed he attacked with some force, quite capable of doing a fair amount of bodily harm.

Sloopy had elected to nest right at the back of the shed and was slowly wasting away from the lack of food and water I was unable to replenish. Apparently geese do not leave their nests once they start sitting and Gustav was so busy playing guard dog he'd forgotten about the husbandly duty of finding food for his wife.

"I can't get into the goose shed and Sloopy hasn't any food or water," I announced at teatime.

"Don't be such a wet," said Aubrey standing up from the table. "You're just scared. Be a bit more positive about it."

"Well you go out there being positive then," I challenged. I followed my irate husband into the paddock but held back a bit as Aubrey opened the main door of the shed.

"Get back you idiot," he shouted at Gustav as he flew at him.

"I see what you mean." Aubrey picked bits of straw and feathers off his jumper. "Stupid old fool. We'll have to sort out some way to catch him."

Later that evening Aubrey appeared with a piece of 1 inch square wood about 4 feet long with a loop of cord fixed so it ran back to his hand through a staple like a noose.

"Behold!" He showed me proudly how it worked. "We have a Gustav catcher. See, when I poke this in the shed I should be able to slip the noose over his head from a distance and catch him."

"Shall we try it in the morning?" I suggested.

"No, let's do it now. Before Sloopy fades away completely. Anyway, I want to try it." Needless to say, this was easier said than done. As Aubrey opened the door Gustav flew at him threatening all sorts of injuries and Aubrey shot back quickly.

"Right. I know what to do. Come over here," he instructed.

"I'm not going in there," I looked horror struck.

"Don't be silly, look if I open the door a tiny bit and push the Gustav catcher in and close the door almost, you can look through the wire netting and guide me to catch him."

The goose house had wire mesh running along the top third of one side, so I peered through to see where the Gustav catcher and the elusive gander were situated and shouted helpful comments like 'left a bit', 'up a bit' and 'back a bit' until a very irate gander was captured.

"We should send this off to the BBC as a suggestion for a game show," I said as we removed Gustav at arm's length, and loosed him into a spare stable, both laughing.

Now Sloopy could be fed and watered, and very relieved she was about that. Unfortunately we soon realised that another mistake was to have left all the geese in the same shed because once one started sitting the others all followed suit, even if they hadn't laid any eggs. There were endless fights over eggs until Aub threw the two unnamed wives out of the shed and put them into the stable with Gustav as they were just stealing Blindy and Sloopy's eggs.

Eventually it was only Sloopy who produced goslings, six ugly little creatures looking like mini prehistoric monsters. Only four of those survived long enough for us to consider their existence as Christmas dinners, two having fallen into their feed trough, where they got stuck, and being such funny shaped little things they were unable to get out and by the time I found them were dead. Consequently, when a friend of ours called and said his brother was looking for some geese, the entire family from Gustav down to the babies rapidly changed hands again, although we kept the goose house as an extension for the ducks.

Chapter Twelve

Mules

The end of July and beginning of August heralded the warm weather, much to Aubrey's delight. Combines were already busy near Cirencester, but Througham corn still had at least another week to go before it would be ripe enough to cut.

Aubrey was champing at the bit to get going, his health and temper not improved by the arrival of his cousin Joe one evening to tell him he was starting to cut the following day, even though Aubrey knew his farm was lower down than Througham.

Aubrey had dreams of driving up and down the golden corn on the big red combine that he had already taken out of the shed and blown all the accumulated dust from ready for action. However he soon realised that Donald was the only one who would get to drive the combine, while he was relegated to driving the tractor and trailer alongside to catch the crop before driving it back to the barn and drier where he tipped it before returning at speed for his next load.

Once the moment arrived and the crop was deemed ready to cut, it felt like the troops moving out to take over the Cotswolds: red, yellow and green combines and tractors streaming off in all directions.

Harvest is a beautiful time of the year. The weather can be difficult but eventually at some point each year it's possible to recall brilliant blue skies contrasting with the different shades of gold of uncut wheat and barley and yellow fields of fallen straw.

I spent quite a lot of my time preparing picnics for Aubrey to take with him each day. Although the combines didn't start cutting until the dew had risen, the machine needed daily maintenance which fell to the experience of Aubrey each morning, and by mid morning the combine would usually be rolling again. Most evenings I was able to join Fiona with a tea time picnic and the combine and tractor would stop for a while and both men would join us sitting in the sunshine, eating tea.

Once the decision had been made to find a new home for Satan and his wives and daughters, Aubrey and I had many discussions about what we could do next.

Aubrey was adamant that now we'd got on the first rung of the ladder as sheep farmers we should try to start a larger flock. Having made sure Fred would not only let us rent an additional bigger field, but also use his barn for lambing, he was not to be swayed.

"We'll get some Mule ewes," Aub announced. "They're the most practical commercial sheep to have and there's a lot around, so we should be able to pick up some draft ewes quite cheaply."

I just raised my eyebrows at him as though he was talking a foreign language, but refrained from commenting at that time. Instead, I said, "First we've got to find a good home for the blacks, although I'd almost say anyone could have Satan, I'm so fed up with him."

Then I added, "But we did promise the lady we bought the ewes from that we'd look after them so we need them to go to someone who really wants them. My black babies are so lovely I could almost keep those."

That problem was actually solved again by Donald who, on contacting the person the blacks had come from, discovered another who was delighted to buy the whole flock, even Satan.

When they came to view them and indeed take them away, they were prepared to pay considerably more than Aub and I had dared to imagine as Satan turned out to be a very good example of the breed and we even managed to secure his pedigree from Uncle John which added to his value. His five ewe lambs were lovely sheep and both sellers and purchasers were delighted with their deal. A few days later, Aub bounced into the kitchen beaming from ear to ear.

"Donald gave me the phone number of a sheep dealer who knows of twenty or so reasonable draft Mules we can buy. I rang him from the farm and he's going to get back in touch in a couple of days," he said excitedly.

"Twenty's a lot, isn't it?" I asked. "Do we want that many? Can we afford that many?"

I was not that well informed on sheep, so numerous discussions were held across the kitchen table when Aubrey enlightened me on both what a Mule and a draft sheep was.

He began by patiently explaining, in layman's terms, that the highest farms in England were hill farms; the slightly better, lower land was termed as upland; while the rest of the country was described as lowland.

I learned about the mountain sheep and began to admire the Swaledales as Aub defined them, remembering his uncle's flock of hardy, arrogant sheep. Dark faces with white noses and white rings like polos around their eyes. The wool of their thick, waterproof coats was worth very little, but it kept them warm and dry.

He explained that while there were lots of different hill breeds, English farmers had found Swaledales to be the best to cross and produce a lowland ewe. "Technically it's called the sheep pyramid but, if you think of a Christmas tree, the fairy on the top is a Swaledale."

He continued to explain that on the hill farms they'd be bred pure, but as they got older they'd often be sold down to Upland farms. They were still living on the hills, but conditions weren't so harsh as the fell tops.

"Do you remember the Lake District area where we saw them?" he asked. He stood up and rifled around on one of the shelves in the dining room where he knew a map might be found. He laid it out on the kitchen table, pointing out different places. "Look at where I mean. The slightly older ewes would cope better there, off the tops and were usually put to a Blue Faced Leicester ram and the lamb they produced was called a Mule."

"Why are they called a Mule? Seems an odd name for a sheep."

"I suppose because it's a crossbreed where you only breed from the females. The ram lambs go for meat."

"Oh. Can't you breed from the ewes and use a Mule ram to breed more Mules?"

"People don't. Generations of farmers have found what works, and crossing Mule with Mule doesn't. Anyway, those producing the Mule lambs have the original breeding stock so they wouldn't need to. Look can we get back to my pyramid?"

"I thought it was a Christmas tree." I grinned.

"Could be either." He grinned back at me. "Do just shut up and listen or I'll give up educating you."

"No honest, I'm really interested. I didn't know you knew so much about sheep. You rarely read books."

"It isn't only books you learn from. My Dad and grandfather and uncles knew more about sheep than I'll ever know, but I learnt a lot from them. Right." He pushed the map towards me, indicating different areas.

He showed me where the Swaledales would be brought down from the tops, pointing out the names of the fells. Down there the older ewes, probably just three or four years, would find life easier on lower ground. The farmers there would mainly put the ewes to a Blue Faced Leicester tup.

He looked at me and stopped me as I started to speak, "And don't ask why they picked that breed, but someone did years ago and found it worked and it now produces the most popular ewe in the country."

"Okay. So is that what we're going to buy?"

"Yes. But older ones. Young mules sell at the North Country sales, like Hawes and Kirkby sheep sale, for a lot of money. They're bought by lowland farms and when they sell their older ewes on, that's where we'll buy from."

Acknowledging the kettle boiling away on the Rayburn, I got up and made the coffee.

Aubrey explained we would be buying draft ewes, so called as older ewes were drafted out of flocks throughout the pyramid. "It's just that when we would come to buy them, they're what is being thrown out at the bottom of the pyramid."

I smiled at him, realising he was looking a bit intense about our discussion. I said brightly, "Going back to our Christmas tree, we could say they're the presents left under the tree for us to have."

"I'm glad you're looking at it like that. I wasn't sure you were quite on board with this new venture," Aubrey said tentatively, raising enquiring eyebrows.

I leant over the table and put my hands on his.

"Of course I'm on board, you idiot. I just feel a bit out of my depth with the prospect of a real flock of sheep. I need a book. I need to study what we will be doing so I don't make too many mistakes and yes, I love the idea. We'll be real sheep farmers by Christmas. I love the Christmas tree idea."

Aubrey stood up and wrapped his arms round me and gave me a deep, passionate kiss. "I know why I married you. When are we having supper?"

Chapter Thirteen

The Arrival

By the time we could see the headlights of the lorry carrying our new flock of North Country Mules along the lane, the evening light was beginning to fade. It was only September but the nights were drawing in and by quarter to eight it was definitely dusk. We rushed out to greet the driver.

"Where d'ya want 'em, mate?" he asked.

Aubrey explained how best to manoeuvre the lorry to unload so the sheep could run straight into the field. The sale of Satan, his wives and their daughters plus the sparse addition of our savings had actually secured twenty elderly ewes, or brokers as they were technically known. Although loosing them into a strange field this late at night was not ideal, we had nowhere else to put them, so as the lorry ramp was lowered the ewes tentatively stepped down onto the road and we guided them through the gateway into the small, securely fenced paddock we'd made ready for them. Probably feeling slightly apprehensive and bewildered, having travelled for most of the day, they soon decided the grass was appetising and settled down quite contentedly mooching around, grazing.

We waved goodbye to the lorry driver having discovered he was driving back to Carlisle that night. He refused our offer of coffee and something to eat saying he was well set up in the lorry and would just like to get on the road. As his tail lights dimmed into the dusk and rounded the corner out of sight we continued to lean on the gate, Aubrey's arm around my shoulders, hugging me tightly, starring at the ewes as they gradually moved further into the field.

"Our first real flock of sheep" he said, grinning. "Can't quite believe we've got them"

"You will when all we can afford for supper will be potatoes and perhaps a few eggs," I said, well aware we would be living very much hand to mouth for a while. Every scrap of our meagre savings had been invested in these old girls and they would need feeding as well.

"That's OK. You know egg and chips is my favourite meal," said Aubrey, laughing, not prepared to be deflated in any way. I also felt relieved, having expressed my slight concern about the monetary side of things and equally happy that now we'd become real farmers. We walked the few yards back to the cottage where the kitchen light shone onto the path to welcome us. Aubrey stopped and put his arms round me.

"You're not unhappy that we've done this, are you?"

"Of course not, you dumbo. We both want to farm and now we really have made a start. I'd prefer not to have another ram like Satan though." I smiled at him. "Give us ten years and we'll have two thousand not twenty."

Laughing, Aubrey opened the door and we trooped inside to be greeted by Florrie and the cats.

"I don't see us with two thousand, just perhaps a couple of hundred of slightly better quality, but these girls will do for now.

Chapter Fourteen

A Ram and Annie

The ewes soon settled in and although flighty to begin with, gradually gained confidence. They looked expectantly for us each morning, knowing a bag of nuts would appear and they would descend on the troughs as though they were starving. In fact, they looked in fair condition, the fresh grass and small supplement of sheep nuts improving them out of all recognition. Having been bought as a 'flying flock' to produce and rear a lamb, then to be sold either with lambs at foot or straight after the lambs were weaned, Aubrey was now talking about them perhaps lasting for two seasons.

"We'll have to see how they do, but they actually look far better than I'd dared to hope," he said.

Donald had already been up to cast his eye over our new flock and given his stamp of approval, something neither Aubrey nor I had expected.

"They'll do you well, boy," he told Aubrey. "They're a tidy bunch. You look after them and they'll surprise you. That dealer who found you these, he was fairly decent to you, that's for sure. You'd better come down the market when I take that ol' Suffolk ram there next week. He's looking a wreck this year but he looked a gem when I bought him last autumn and he's left good lambs. Just can't bear looking at him any longer, but he'll not cost you much and he'll do all you want one to do. Better than buying something you don't know which might have hidden problems. This chap's problems aren't hidden, they're obvious."

Donald had already explained to Aubrey that to be fair to both his boss and Aubrey, he was taking the ram to the market where he could be valued by prospective purchasers. He'd told Aub if 'the bloody thing' had been his he'd have given it to Aubrey, but it wasn't.

I arranged with Laura to have the morning off and joined Aubrey on the trip to the market. Donald was taking the ram down in the trailer so pointed out that even if he bought a couple of new rams, there would still be room for the old boy to travel home. I'd seen the old Suffolk and realised he could look nothing like he had the previous year when Donald had bought him, but he was sound and straight, if not the strong upstanding animal he was when purchased. Twelve months of living on the Cotswold escarpment had told on him and while he'd never been neglected, nor had he been pampered. As Donald said, "Och, he's just fallen apart."

In kindness to Aubrey, Donald had entered him in the cull sale, where his destiny was meat if we didn't buy him and the auctioneers knew of Aubrey's hopes to buy him.

The culls were sold in the pens, the auctioneer walking along a boardway above the pens, selling the animals by pen number, which could be ten females or sometimes, like this, just the one animal.

"Right, what have we here? A fine specimen," he said jovially and took bids in single pounds, knocking him down to Aubrey for under £30.

"Can't promise he'll father twins for all of them, but a sound

75

investment and come from a good home." He then moved on to the next pen as the on-looking company chuckled.

Aub and I were delighted. Donald suggested the ram went back to Lower Througham for a couple more weeks and was introduced to our ewes in October.

"That should get your lambing out of the way before we start in earnest down at the farm," he said.

Laura appeared in the yard the next day, just as I came in with Hector and Smokey, saying she had something I might like, so to come indoors once the horses were settled. Intrigued, I tentatively opened the kitchen door to be greeted by a small black and white collie, with beautiful symmetrical markings, a soft coat and a smile that beamed from ear to ear.

"What do you think?" asked Laura, pouring hot water into two cups for instant coffee. "She's one of my mother's obedience dogs, but Mum says she's too small for her. Apparently the dogs have to walk alongside their handler with their head close to their hand and Mum has to bend down to have her hand in the right position!"

I was aware that Laura's mother was a top class obedience trainer, having won at Crufts the previous spring.

"Wow, it's a bit technical this obedience isn't it?" I'd met Laura's mother, so I could imagine that this little dog might be a long way down from her 5ft 10ins stature. The little bitch pushed a cold wet nose into my hand to encourage me to stroke, although I didn't need much encouragement.

"Mum's looking for a good home for her, but she's bred to work sheep, so now you have your new flock we wondered if you'd like a sheepdog?"

"Crikey. I don't think even Aub's thought about that." I bent down and fondled the little dog, although to be fair she wasn't that small. The collie looked up at me with her soft brown eyes.

"She's really sweet isn't she?"

"Mum's done all the basic obedience training with her, but I don't think she's seen sheep, so it'll be a bit trial and error. Can you afford to keep a second dog?"

"Probably not; but that's never stopped us before. Can I just ask Aubrey first? Shall we see if Florrie likes her? What's she called?"

"Yes, let's go outside. Florrie likes most dogs doesn't he? Mum called her Annie, but I expect you could give her a sheepdog type name without any problem."

Florrie immediately fell in love with the little collie, so we agreed that Annie would stay with Laura for the weekend when Aubrey and I could discuss the further addition to our family. After a very short discussion, Aubrey's eyes sparkling with anticipation, we drove back to Laura's that evening. It was obviously love at first sight, for both parties. Aubrey was quite overcome.

"This will be the first time we've taken on something that could be useful," he said, laughingly. Annie returned home with us and soon became one of the family, but particularly Aub's dog.

He decided that her training as a sheep dog should start immediately. The fact that she was obedient helped immensely, but she also had a deep desire to move sheep. Donald suggested Aub took her to work with him as, with the ewes not in lamb yet, it as an ideal time to work her with the other dogs. Both men were amazed at the way she seemed such a natural worker. At eighteen months she was older than some are started but that worked well in her favour as she was stronger with the sheep than a younger dog. She also stayed as Annie as she knew her name and responded to it, certainly better than Florrie ever did to his.

Chapter Fifteen

Fred goes on Holiday

It was a blustery November evening, the fire crackling in the grate in the sitting room, when Fred arrived.

I was in the kitchen checking the potatoes were cooked and ready to join the pie browning in the oven. Appetising smells and a golden glow filled the house. Suddenly a loud banging on the outer door of the front porch heralded his arrival.

Letting him in, I battled to close the outer door, the wind trying to rip it from my hands. Eventually I succeeded, and leant back against it with relief as I welcomed Fred, inviting him to come through to the kitchen.

"Come in Fred, before we all get blown away."

"Aye I will. 'Tis a fairly wild night out there, but as I was strolling past I thought I'd just call in," said Fred, then glancing at my clean kitchen floor once I'd opened the inner door, halted in his tracks and started to fumble with his clothing.

He abandoned his greatcoat, padded waistcoat, woolly hat and gloves and considered for a minute whether it was best to remove or retain his wellingtons. As they were actually fairly clean and dry he must have decided they were in a better state than his socks, so he kept them on.

Aub came through to the kitchen, his raised eyebrow questioning Fred's statement. Fred never strolled anywhere.

If he called on you there was a very good reason for it, but it could take a few cups of coffee, or something stronger, before we discovered the reason for his visit.

"Coffee, Fred?" Aubrey asked. "I'm just putting the kettle on. Sugar?"

"Thank you kindly, just the three."

"Sit down Fred," I indicated one of the chairs at the kitchen table. Had he removed his boots I would have suggested going through to the sitting room, but on principal I decided the kitchen would do. Anyway, get Fred by the fire and we'd have him all night.

"It's certainly blowing this evening," I said.

"Aye, there'll be a few of these old elms down in the morning mind." Fred ignored my suggestion of the kitchen chair and moved into the sitting room. Without ceremony he removed one of the cats from an armchair and settled himself centrally in front of the fire, his wellingtons resting against the fender.

"Here's the coffee" said Aubrey, bearing three hot mugs.

"How's things then, Fred?" he asked, handing me my cup before sitting in the adjacent chair. "Got much on at the moment?"

Fred took a quick slurp of his coffee and recoiled at speed in obvious discomfort. "Blimey, it's a hot cup of coffee you make."

There was no answer to that so he considered the previous question. "Not much on at the moment. Very quiet in fact. Too cold to go walling in this weather. Much happening on the farm?"

"There's always plenty to do, Fred,' replied Aubrey patiently. "Still catching up with the fencing that should have been done earlier when it was so wet. Feeding the stock is starting to take up a good part of each day though."

Fred seemed to be mulling this over in his mind.

"How's Elizabeth?" I asked after his wife. "Haven't seen her for a while."

Fred's face brightened up.

"Well you know, she ain't been so good for a while. She could do with a break. That's really what I've come to see you about." He bravely attempted another mouthful of coffee, happily finding it at a more acceptable temperature.

"Well," he said again. "We thought we'd have a couple of weeks away in Cornwall. Take the boys as well. It's nice and quiet on the beach this late in the year."

That seemed a bit of an understatement, but Fred constantly surprised us, so we refrained from commenting.

"When are you going?" Aubrey asked, giving the fire a bit of a poke so that sparks jumped out, making Fred withdraw his feet quickly.

"We thought we'd go on Saturday. We've rented a cottage for a couple of weeks. I thought as I looked after your ducks while you were away pr'aps you could just pop along and feed the chickens?" He glanced hopefully at me.

"Yes of course, Fred," I said, thinking that we'd got off lightly if this had been the only surprise he had in store for us.

Fred settled back in his chair, satisfied that he'd elicited the answer he required. He slurped away at his coffee, happily chatting now about the state of the country and his thoughts on politics. After a little thought he declined a second cup of coffee and rose to go.

Heading for the porch to re-attire himself in his full winter woollies, he turned just as he left, and added, "That's OK with the chickens then? Good, good. And perhaps you could just check the cattle – and them three cows, they're being milked twice a day, but you know where everything is, don't you?"

When we had gone away for four days in October we'd asked Wilf, Fred's older son, if he could feed the ducks and let them out in the mornings and shut them up at nights, as he walked past their house on his way to and from work. This he kindly did and was well rewarded financially on our return. We were later made aware that one evening Fred had taken it upon himself to shut them up. This was obviously payback!

So Fred and family drove off to Cornwall quite happily looking forward to two weeks of lazing on a cold November beach while Aub and I looked forward to two weeks of extremely early mornings and late nights.

Of course, as Fred already knew, we were both working full time. Aubrey was on the farm 8 am to 5pm and although my hours could be a little more flexible as long as the work was done, that could also mean some evenings I could be late home. I thought it might be easier for me to milk in the mornings than Aub, after all Fred only had three cows. He did have a milking machine and in one of my previous jobs I had milked two house cows at the weekends. I soon changed my mind after we attempted to milk on the Saturday evening, only to discover that while the cows were no problem, the machinery and pipe-work was a major one.

Nothing really worked. Due to old age and lack of management the rubber pipes had perished. Hand milking would have been a lot quicker, but the cows weren't used to that. Judging by the expressions on their faces they were obviously considering us to be total amateurs, and they were right. Hand milking might just have been the final straw. As it was, the amount of milk they were prepared to let down for total strangers was minimal and it wasn't until day three there was enough to make it worthwhile putting the churn out for collection.

However, they were obviously quite used to the equipment falling to pieces around them and the oldest Guernsey didn't blink an eye when a pipe split causing suction to cease and the cluster to fall off between her legs. She'd seen that all before! She simply continued eating her meagre feed of nuts. After a few days of trial and error we worked out a system whereby we were able to use one unit successfully, so we had to play 'all change' with the cows once one had been milked, with the next one moving as close to the unit as possible rather than moving the equipment from one cow to another, as by this time Aub had cut so much perished rubber off the pipes it didn't reach very far. This would have been aggravating enough at the best of times, but at six o'clock in the morning, when we had a full day's work to look forward to rounded pleasantly off by the evening milking, it proved a little testing to the sense of humour and conversation was sparse.

"We'll have to lift the milk bucket up onto a bale if I have to cut the pipe any shorter," Aub muttered.

There was also a little black Angus cow to be brought in and two calves taken out of pens to suckle her. They were enthusiastic enough to go and see her for their meals, but recapturing them and returning them to their pen proved a sort of Olympic challenge.

Then the bullocks had to be checked, four small Angus types and a bigger, less healthy looking Charolais cross. He was definitely sickening for something and had been for weeks.

Aubrey had diagnosed 'wooden tongue', a disease of the soft tissues of the mouth, which can be cured quite rapidly with veterinary treatment. Fred had also thought it could be this, but Fred had his own primeval methods of doctoring his stock, and consequently the poor beast was getting thinner and thinner and looking nearer to death each day.

That was until the evening when we couldn't find him at all. It was a crisp, frosty moonlit evening, quite unlike the usual wet, foggy pitch-black times we usually had disasters. In fact, if we hadn't been so worried about the loss of the beast (Fred was convinced it was on the mend and going to make a good price at market, 'a big bullock like him'), it would have been a lovely evening for a walk around the fields.

It was about half past seven when we finished milking and let the cows out again. As we were later doing the evening milking than Fred usually was, owing to other daytime occupations, the cows were always standing by the old milking parlour waiting to come in. It wasn't until we'd let them back into the field that we saw to the other stock. Aubrey went round with the torch to check the bullocks while I washed up in the dairy, but on this occasion I'd finished before he returned so went to join him in the field.

"That Charolais isn't here," he groaned.

I asked him where he'd looked and he assured me he'd looked all round the field and in the barn.

"Damn thing must have got out," he said.

That was no great feat for any of Fred's stock, his fences being more in his imagination than reality.

"I bet he's gone to die somewhere," I said, thinking of elephants that go miles to burial grounds when death is imminent.

"Well I wish he could have died here, if he had to do it," retorted Aubrey, agreeing that it was quite possible that this could have happened.

"Why couldn't he have waited until Fred got home before he snuffed it?" It was no good complaining about it; we'd just have to find him.

"We'll take the tractor," said Aubrey. We'd gone along to Fred's on the Ford 4000 tractor Aubrey used at work and was bringing home at nights to save time.

"We'll see better walking," I suggested tentatively, knowing of Aub's dislike for this mode of transport.

"If you think I'm walking round Fred's fields you are mistaken," I was told, so we climbed on the tractor and started our search.

"Oh God, what if he's fallen in the quarry?" I said, panicking, so we went there first, but could see nothing there. It was a good thing it was a cream coloured Charolais and not the black Angus we were looking for, but still we saw nothing in the moonlight.

After about twenty minutes we headed back towards the cow's original field.

"Well, let's try the two acre," said Aubrey. "He's probably on his back in the brook."

We went down the hill to the long thin field separated from the cows' field by a small brook, a dilapidated stone wall and a scrubby old hedge. At one end there appeared to be no division at all.

"You can't take the tractor through there," I screamed at him above the noise of the engine, horrified. "It's all mud where the brook drains away and half the wall has fallen in there."

"Well, you needn't think I'm walking up there."

"You'll have to. You can't possibly drive through there. There's nothing solid to go on."

I knew this only too well, having lost Florrie in this field earlier in the year and waded up to my knees in mud to find him. Even while I was still offering reasons why we couldn't go that way Aubrey drove on. About thirty seconds later we were at a grinding halt sinking in the mud.

"Damn. I didn't think it was like that. I thought we could get through here," he muttered. For once I refrained from any comment.

"We'll have to go and get Fred's tractor, and pull it out," he said.

"Surely Fred's old tractor won't pull yours out?" Aubrey's tractor was a 4000, far more powerful than Fred's old Fergie 35.

"Course it will. Might even move itself in reverse, but we'll chain his on just to make sure."

We trekked back up the hill, which was warming as the evening chill was now beginning to bite. The tractor had stood idle for the past ten days, but with a little persuasion it burst into life. We found a large chain for pulling with, which Aubrey used to hitch both tractors together, the 4000 now having sunk more securely in the mud while we were away.

"It won't rear up will it?" I asked in very worried tones. That sort of thing had happened to me before and it terrified me that the tractor was going to come over backwards.

"No – it's perfectly safe," Aubrey assured me. "Look, I've hitched on right at the bottom here. When I wave, pull in bottom gear. Nothing can go wrong."

Aubrey very patiently explained it all to me, knowing that if I got sufficiently into a twitter about anything mechanical

I wouldn't get on and drive it. He nearly spoilt it by saying 'nothing could go wrong' though.

We were lucky that the moon was still shining down on us. It was like a comedy act being performed under floodlights. At the appointed signal the 35 started to pull, but owing to the incline of the hill, the slippery surface of frost forming on the grass and the hold the mud had on the 4000, all that happened was Fred's tractor skittered sideways, its front wheels coming off the ground.

I stopped the engine and jumped off.

"I'm not driving that – it's rearing," I screamed at Aubrey. Not only was I frightened, I was cold, tired and thoroughly fed up. Sympathy was short, but luckily he'd accepted that Fred's tractor obviously wasn't man enough for the job, so we disconnected the two tractors and drove Fred's back to the barn. Aubrey then had a brainwave.

"I'll get Mike. He can get the four wheel drive out. That ought to move it." So off we trundled on the cold, cab-less 35 to get Mike from the cottages on the hill.

It was about 9.30 pm by then and Mike had just settled down in front of a roaring log fire to watch something good on TV. Still, he supposed he'd better come and help, so we all trooped back along the road in a stately procession, Mike on the big four wheel drive and Aubrey and me on the little, very draughty 35.

The big tractor pulled the 4000 out with very little ado, much to our relief. While explaining to Mike how the situation had arisen we remembered we still hadn't found the Charolais.

"You'll have to have a good look in the morning," Aubrey told me. We both agreed we could do nothing further that night.

With grateful thanks to Mike, while he and Aubrey re-organised the tractors, I nipped round to shut the chickens up, having forgotten to do them earlier. And there he was, cream coat glinting eerily in the moonlight, standing in the chicken run. He was still alive, so I persuaded him to leave the run, shut the chickens up and threw the bullock a large wodge of hay to keep him happy for the night.

The epilogue to the story was that two days after Fred's return I looked in the field for the Charolais, and being unable to see him asked Fred how he was.

"Oh him. I took him to the knackers," he told me. "No meat on him. Once they get these wasting diseases there's nothing you can do for them. Meant to take him before we went away, just didn't have time."

Chapter Sixteen

Christmas

As Christmas loomed on the horizon, Aubrey started handling the ducks before they were let out in the mornings to see how fat they were getting. The ducks appeared to think this was hilarious. A sort of 'catch and tickle us' game. After the night they all roosted on the roof of the house, Aubrey had had to trim one wing on each duck to unbalance them, so they couldn't fly. No real fear that they'd fly away when they were so well fed, but it was annoying when they sat on the guttering of the roof and left rude messages on the bedroom windows.

Preparing the ducks for Christmas dinners was a very complex job. By now Aubrey didn't have the heart to kill the ducks himself. He might seem hard-bitten sometimes but he's always had a soft centre. He'd seen them hatch. Watched them take their first waddle, their first bath and had them gallop towards him, wagging their tails when called for their food.

They even did this on the day he caught them and stuffed them in a sack to go to be slaughtered. It would have taken a very hard hearted person to slaughter them himself. So an elderly gentleman who lived in Bisley agreed to come and kill them, leaving just the plucking and dressing to do.

If we hadn't been so broke we would never have done this. The ducks would probably all have become lifetime pets, but at that time we were trying hard to make a small living from our animals and everything had to go. As it was, neither of us could bring ourselves to eat the ducks, but all had rapidly sold, and the money would help with sheep feed.

I joined Aub in plucking the ducks, mainly because he'd by then decided he didn't really want to be doing it either. Sitting down with him in the barn I started to pluck my first duck, until it quacked! I screamed, threw the duck onto the straw and ran out of the barn, followed by a hysterical husband, who insisted the duck was dead, as it was, and it was just the air inside it that had made the quack.

It was at that point I laid down the ground rules that anything to be cooked arrived in the kitchen oven-ready in future.

On Christmas eve, having put the horses to bed early and exchange good wishes and presents with Laura and her family, who were in charge for the next two days, I arrived home just before dark. I'd called at the local farm shop to collect the vegetables I'd ordered earlier in the week. The fresh food shopping took a bit of organising when we both worked long hours, even though it was only the two of us this year for Christmas because his parents were visiting a sick relation and mine were having an aunt to stay.

Wishing Janet in the shop a very Happy Christmas, I stopped briefly at the house to drop off the vegetables and Florrie before picking up a torch to go and feed the ewes. Aubrey wouldn't be home for another half an hour so I collected sheep nuts and hay from the barn, which I carried out to the field for our new flock, now all hopefully in lamb. I shouted to alert them that tea was coming, and was ready to start tipping nuts into the trough when I realised the sheep were conspicuous by their absence. In fact, it was the first time for weeks that I'd reached the troughs without being pushed over or found myself astride one of the woolly beasts as they barged between my legs, fighting for position to feed.

I shook the bucket of nuts and kicked the trough encouragingly but received no response. With the large torch on main beam I shone the light round the boundary fence. Still seeing no sign of the animals, I trekked along the perimeter until I reached a small section of wall that had collapsed onto the ground, obviously the escape route. After struggling up the field with a hurdle that could be used at a later point to block the gap, I turned for home to make a cup of tea and hopefully stuff the turkey before Aub and I embarked on a marathon search for the escapees. Aub and sheepdog Annie appeared at the kitchen door; he obviously thought I was joking when I said the flock had left home. While I made the tea and a quick sandwich, he and Annie went to check I'd not just 'missed' twenty sheep, feeling quite sure he'd find them standing in the field.

On his return I was assured that this was no time to fiddle about stuffing a turkey when the sheep could be heading off along the main road. He downed a scalding cup of tea, and anticipating severe indigestion devoured a sandwich, then we headed off.

"Come on Annie," said Aubrey, and armed with torches we'd all headed for the great outdoors.

"We'd better take the car, they could have gone for miles." As ever, he was never a great one for walking, but this time grudgingly agreed with me that it might be a good idea to check the adjacent fields on foot first.

It was a beautiful evening. Crisp and frosty underfoot, with bright moonlight making the search a lot easier. Unfortunately there were also banks of low cloud which blotted out the moon for several minutes on end, usually when it was most critical to see where we were going, and inevitably I found a large hole to put my foot in.

"Ouch, hang on a minute. I've twisted my ankle."

"We haven't got time for you to be a drama queen. Come on."

I realised Aubrey was thin on sympathy and I would just have to hobble on. After searching the front field, we carried on over a hurdle into the Quarry field, only to be horrified yet again by Fred's lack of fencing maintenance. Broken down gates and collapsed stone walls did really mean the sheep could have gone in any number of directions, but we followed the most used track as sheep do tend to follow paths.

"Bloody hell, if Fred could just repair his boundary fences it would be something. The ewes could be anywhere." Aubrey was really worried now, thinking the sheep might have reached the main road and caused an accident or been killed themselves.

After almost an hour of trudging round fields, flashing torches and getting excited to see eyes light up in a beam, only to be disheartened again when a deer or fox ran off, we were exhausted. We came to the conclusion that the sheep must have gone through the almost non-existent fence of the seven acre and on through Ron's field. Aubrey knew there was a gate open at the far end leading straight onto the road.

Hurrying back to the car we loaded up and drove to the farm on the main road. The barn lights were ablaze, and Ron and his son Tim had just finished milking as we arrived.

"Ewes? No haven't seen any nor heard anything from

anyone who's found 'em. Come on in." Ron ushered us into the farmhouse kitchen, dog and all, to have a Christmas drink and think about the whereabouts of our flock.

The kitchen was warm and welcoming. The Rayburn was not only throwing out a lovely cosy glow, it had also just cooked the steaming mince pies that Anne, Ron's wife insisted we had to go with the generous glasses of whisky poured out for us. Ron and Tim asked Aubrey's opinion on the merits of different types of milking parlours until he reminded them it was sheep we were looking for. Ron rubbed his hand on his bristly chin.

"Well let's think where these blighters could be," he muttered, deep in thought. "They can't be out on the road or we'd have had someone round shouting about them," he added sensibly.

While Aubrey and I happily ate yet another mince pie and drank a cup of coffee, (Aubrey felt more alcohol was not ideal when he was driving), Ron rang a few neighbours to see if they'd seen the sheep. No one had seen any, but someone mentioned that Phil, in the next village, had said something about some strays. So with Christmas wishes, shouts of good cheer and instructions to return if we needed help, we took off in the direction of Phil's farm.

Of course Phil had been talking about something completely different from our sheep. He'd found two stray bullocks which wasn't much good to us. Still as it was Christmas Eve, he felt we should have a quick drink with him. We tried hard to decline this, but he assured us a quick drink would clarify the situation.

Having hit the cold winter air after leaving Ron's, Aub and I were both convinced any more drinks would make it difficult to differentiate between 20 and 2000 sheep, but realised we couldn't refuse his hospitality, although Aubrey poured his sloe gin into my glass when Phil wasn't looking. I wasn't driving. Hopefully I'd still be able to walk to the car! By now we were desperate to know the whereabouts of our small flock.

"They could have crossed the drilled field opposite and aimed up towards the common," I suddenly thought. "Scottie's got sheep up there."

"Of course they could," Aubrey agreed. Having seen the state of Fred's fencing the ewes would barely have had to push against it to escape for the common.

We drove back across the main road and headed for home, deciding to leave the car and walk from there. I was definitely feeling the worst for wear after a whisky and two generous sloe gins, but I trudged after Aubrey again in the direction of the common. The only one really enjoying all this strenuous exercise was Annie, who thought it was great. When we reached the common I started to clamber over the metal gate into the field.

"Don't climb gates, I've told you that before. You'll damage it," grouched Aubrey, by now quite frantic to find his sheep and fed up with walking round the countryside. I was beyond words. Aubrey then discovered, as I had, that it was padlocked and climbed over the hinge end as well. We walked round the track and shone the torch across the field. No sign of anything. We walked the boundary of the field to another gate.

"They couldn't have got into this field, could they?" said Aubrey.

I agreed it was unlikely, but we decided to go in and shine the torch around. It looked like something out of Fantasia. We were greeted by the glistening reflections of eyes, far more than we needed, but we were fairly confident the Christmas celebrations were responsible for that. The frost, crisp underfoot, sparkled in the torch light and one ewe was even wearing a halo of ivy stolen from the wall. All seemed quite happy where they were, so we carried on down the lane to Scottie's house to tell him he had trespassers.

Once again we were greeted in the characteristic way of neighbouring farmers, the door thrown open and an invitation to join the family round a glowing fire, with the traditional hot punch and mince pies.

"Sorry, I tried to get in touch with you earlier, but you were still out. I found them marauding round Fred's far field and thought they'd be safer in with mine. At least my field has a fence around it! They'll be fine there," Scottie assured us. "There's plenty of rough grass out there and hay in the racks. You probably did see a few more out there. I've got fifty ewes in that field, so we can have fun sorting them out after Christmas." We were glad to agree with this and later parted with Christmas wishes at almost midnight.

Unsurprisingly, I fell into a deep sleep as soon as my head touched the pillow, the cocktail of whisky, sloe gin and punch working their magic. The turkey could be stuffed in the morning!

Chapter Seventeen

Lambing Dramas

"Fiona, is Donald there?" I pleaded. Fiona was a darling but so softly spoken and generally laid back that the time it took her to answer my call was killing me.

"Yes, I'll just get him for you. Is your young man alright?"

"He's fine but I really need to speak to Donald."

"Right … I'll just get him for you."

I sat down at Elizabeth's table and shook my head when she offered me a mug of hot tea. Although I would have loved one, we needed to get on. It seemed to be at least five minutes before Donald picked up the receiver, although it was probably seconds.

"What's up lass?" he asked in his broad Scottish drawl.

"Oh Donald, I'm really sorry but please, can you come up to Fred's and help me? I've got a ewe that should have lambed but she wasn't opened up and still hasn't. I think it's a ring womb. She was uncomfortable this morning, but not open sufficiently when I went to work and when Elizabeth said all was well and that three had lambed today I thought she was one of them, but I've just got here and she still hasn't lambed and I still can't get my hand inside and I don't know what to do …"

I wiped the tears away from my cheeks and sniffed loudly.

"Sorry," I apologised.

"Well if she's been on since this morning she won't hurt till I've finished my tea." Donald was nothing if not matter of fact. "I'll be with you in ten minutes." And the receiver went down. I looked at Elizabeth in despair.

"He's going to be ten minutes, I thought he'd come straight up."

Elizabeth placed the mug of hot tea on the table in front of me with a slice of her homemade sponge cake, oozing with homemade blackcurrant jam.

"You sit here a minute and have this. If a man says he'll be ten minutes he'll be twenty, so don't you panic. If Donald thought he ought to come straight away he would have done. If anyone can sort it out Donald can. I'm just sorry I didn't notice she wasn't one that had lambed. She's just been picking at the hay when I've looked in. You have that tea and cake, then we can go outside and you can check the others until Donald arrives." Elizabeth sat with me at the table, occasionally flinging her arm out to remove a cat that was brave enough to jump up and try to join us.

"How's your man today?"

This was the main cause of all the problems. Only two days before we were due to start lambing, with Aub so excited about it, he'd been taken ill with some mystery bug which left him horizontal in bed. It wasn't really 'flu, but the symptoms were similar, but so drastic I'd called the doctor out to visit, something almost unheard of, but as Aub couldn't stand up I was never going to get him to the surgery and had threatened to call an ambulance.

Our local doctor was very good and down to earth. Himself unsure, although looking back it could have been some sort of meningitis, he prescribed strong antibiotics, which I drove to Stroud to collect immediately, and indefinite bed rest.

"I can't stay in bed," Aub protested weakly. "We start lambing in two days."

"You don't," he was told. "If you don't do as you're told, or if you get any worse, you'll be in hospital, but you're probably better off here if you behave."

Doctor Pike addressed him very sternly then explained to me that Aub was not to leave his bed for at least a week. Lots of fluids and I was warned to ring him if Aub's temperature rose dramatically.

"Hopefully you'll feel better in the next few days, but I mean what I say about staying in bed. Lambing will just have to be directed from your bed!" and he left saying he would pop in on his rounds the following day unless I called him before.

Amazingly, probably because he felt so awful, Aub just lay back on the pillows, took the tablets and slept.

I rang Laura and explained the situation, saying I wouldn't be over for the next few days as I didn't feel I could leave Aub for longer than it took to check all was well in the barn at Fred's, where the twenty ewes were in residence, and had been for a few days, as it was going to be easier to lamb them there. Hopefully they would lamb fairly quickly as we'd been aware that they'd all been raddled fairly close together, just a couple returning to the next cycle.

Once again, for about the twentieth time, I read the veterinary book Aub had given me for Christmas, which detailed lambing problems and medication and thanked my lucky stars that Donald had been able to fit me in with his other students on an early Agricultural Training Board lambing course. Actually handling a lamb, albeit a dead one, inside a phantom ewe, I'd gained sufficient confidence to understand many of the awkward ways a ewe can present a lamb. (Obviously none of them read books on how it should be done properly, with two front legs followed by the head, with the second twin waiting patiently for his turn.) Oh no, I learnt that they can come backwards, with one leg back, with both legs back, rather like a bullet, or just totally tangled up with the second, or even the third lamb. Having gained more of an insight into these problems I felt sure I could be of help to Aub when the time came to lamb our flock. It had never occurred to me that I might be the one doing all the lambing!

Thankfully Aub's condition improved considerably in the first twenty four hours, although I secretly congratulated myself on having got the doctor out and antibiotics into him so quickly. Without this, things could have been very different. When Doctor Pike called the following day he told me he felt we'd gone past the crisis period, something he didn't share with Aub, simple telling him if he left his bed for anything other than a visit to the loo or a quick wash for the next week he would be transferred to hospital. This was enough to make him do as he was told.

The ewes were quite content in Fred's barn, where Aub had managed to sort out a water trough and put a row of old cattle feed barriers upside down so they could reach feed laid out just outside the pen. We'd put up six individual lambing pens, which should be sufficient for the number of sheep, the small bales of hay were close by and I realised I could manage the sheep quite happily. Then lambing started.

It could have been quite daunting having to do everything myself, but Elizabeth was a gem.

"S'no good asking Fred for any help and don't listen to him if he offers any advice. He won't have a clue. Never done anything with sheep in his life. My dad had a fair flock of sheep and I helped him at home for years, so I remember sommat of it and I'm sure more'll come back to me," she assured me, volunteering to keep an eye on things when I wasn't around. She also kindly said to call her at nights if I needed help, something that hadn't really occurred to me, but of course I'd have to be around twenty-four hours a day.

Luckily the old Mules knew exactly what to do and were an excellent start for a total novice, which I definitely was. But the excitement of seeing those first lambs early in the morning, when the ewe had done it all on her own, polished them, fed them and was waiting for her breakfast was more amazing than I ever expected.

Having checked Aub was still breathing, something I'd been doing at periods throughout the night, I crept out of bed in the dark, the alarm having woken me at five, dressed in warm clothing, let the dogs out for a wee and drove the old pickup along to Fred's. I'd been concerned that the alarm would wake Aub, and smothered it as soon as it went off, but by now was aware that he could almost sleep through an earthquake when fit and healthy, so drugged to the eyeballs he was not going to be worried by the clock.

This lovely kind speckled faced ewe with her two black faced lambs beside her stood to one corner of the shed, out of harm's way. She was murmuring softly to them, and allowed me to spray their navels with the strong iodine, then when I picked them up, aware they were both full, she followed me to the individual pen which would be her home for the next day. I quickly glanced around the shed to see if anyone else was planning to produce, although later knowledge made me aware that once I appeared nothing else occurred to them except breakfast.

Having filled a small bucket with clean fresh water for the ewe with lambs and fed her, I fed the rest of the sheep along the feeder, checked the water trough was clean and topped up the hayrack at the back of the main pen. Having glanced along their backsides as I did this, I could see one or two with pinker udders, although they were so well endowed with fluffy knickers and tails it was difficult to see more, but nothing looked to be imminently planning to lamb.

I put a handful of soft fresh hay in with the family and smiling happily drove home for a cup of tea and bacon sandwich, before waking Aub to tell him all was going really well. Naïve as I was, I was convinced I could do anything. Later that week I was to be proved wrong.

I apologised profusely to Laura, feeling I'd left her in the lurch with the horses, although she assured me she could muck them out and was just putting Hector in the school for an hour and the ponies out in the field, so not to worry. We had agreed that while Aub was so reliant on me and the lambing was happening, I would leave it a few more days before going back to the yard.

"I feel fine," Aub tried to convince me three days later. "Honestly if that stupid doctor wasn't being such a pain I'd be back at work and sorting our sheep."

"Ha ha, dream on. You can still barely do more than make it to the bathroom and have a quick wash before collapsing back to bed, so don't kid yourself."

"Well if nothing is happening in the barn, you could go over to the yard and check your precious horses are OK. If you leave me a sandwich and a cup of coffee I expect I'll survive."

Aub was getting so grumpy and frustrated from not being able to do anything, I felt it would be great to get away for a few hours, so decided I would do that.

Later the following morning, after checking all was well in the barn, the seven ewes that had already lambed were happy in another section with their lambs and the previous night's newcomers content in their individual pens I double checked a ewe who looked uncomfortable, sitting down then getting up. (My lambing skills had barely been called upon, although I had proudly extricated a leg back for one of the ewes.)

Having caught the ewe and persuaded her to lie down so I could check the situation, I discovered that she hadn't really opened up yet, so left Elizabeth with instructions to keep an eye on things while I drove across the valley to the yard.

Hoping I'd have time to take Hector for a ride I'd asked Mary to call at the cottage to check all was well with Aub and take him up the sandwich I had left wrapped up in the kitchen for him. A ride in the glorious countryside was definitely what I needed, but I finished the horses early, drove home just taking time to quickly pop upstairs with a cup of tea for Aub before driving to the barn.

"Mary did you proud then!" I took in the crumbs left from a quiche she had obviously dropped in for him and the remains of a cake.

"Good thing somebody looks after me." He smiled and assured me he was fine and actually feeling better than he had for a while.

"How'd the old horse go then?"

"Good. It felt wonderful to get away for a bit. I rang Elizabeth at lunch time and she said two more had lambed, all on their own, dear old things, and another looks like doing it soon. I expect one of those was one I had on this morning."

"Give me a shout if you need a hand." I laughed, and said I'd be back soon. But that was not to be. The ewe that had looked uncomfortable that morning still hadn't lambed and obviously all was not well with her. Kneeling down beside her, with Elizabeth holding her head, I tried hard to open up the cervix but with very little luck. I could just get two fingers inside, certainly not open enough to extract a lamb, but what I could feel was most odd. Nothing I had come across before. It actually felt like just a tail. I realised I needed help and Donald was the one to call.

I'd had time to calm down a bit, feed and check the new arrivals and provide a bucket of warm water by the time Donald arrived, when I went into overdrive again with thanks, apologies and explanations.

"I don't know why I can't open her up but all I can feel is something like a tail. I'm sure it's a ring womb," I finished with, as Donald instructed me to hold the ewe while he examined her.

"Well your lambing book has been well read. It is a ring womb and you're right about the tail. There's a little offender there who is causing all the problems."

"Can you do anything?" I felt myself near to sobbing again.

"We'll see." Always pragmatic, Donald's emotions often seemed to be lacking. For what seemed to be an age he worked away, gently opening the cervix until he was able to pull out a small blood covered lamb which he threw onto the straw. I leant over to try to instil life into it, but realised it was past resuscitation.

"Oh it's dead," I gasped. "Oh how stupid of me not to realise something was wrong earlier. I've killed it," and tears flooded down my face, my breath coming in gulps that I thought would never stop. I'd killed one of our lambs. My stupidity and lack of knowledge had killed one of our lambs. How was I ever going to tell Aub?

"That was the reason she hadn't opened up properly. Lamb got stuck coming tail and bum first, no way she was going to get that out on her own. She killed it, not you. Been pushing against it for a long time, probably before you'd even have noticed she looked uncomfortable this morning. Hey, don't beat yourself up about it, there's another one in here."

My shoulders still heaving I looked at him in amazement as he started to pull a second, larger lamb from the ewe.

"Oh thank goodness, she'd have been so sad without a baby." Donald threw the lamb in my direction and I cleaned its nose and offered it to the ewe who started to lick it immediately.

"This was your real problem." Donald then pulled a third lamb from the ewe and passed it to me.

"Too many lambs. She had three, two good'ns and the little squatty thing that caused all the problems. Don't you go blaming yourself for that littl'n. You've saved the ewe and she's got two good lambs all because you noticed something wasn't right, which a lot of people wouldn't have done. Your man'll give you a pat on the back."

Donald stood up and washed his hands in the warm water. "How is he today?"

"I think he's really feeling a bit better now," I said. "I've just got to stop him being stupid and rushing back to work. Oh Donald, thank you so much. There was no way I could have done that myself."

"Don't you believe it. You're pretty resourceful. If I hadn't been here you'd have figured it out. Tell your man he's to stay in bed as long as the doctor says. I don't want to see him till he's signed off properly." He glanced at the ewe happily sitting up licking her lambs.

"I'd give her a few minutes to sort herself out if I was you. She'll be OK in here with the others for a bit. I've given her a shot of antibiotics; she'll be fine. Milks on both sides. She's got a great family. I'll sort this," Donald said, picking up the dead lamb as he headed out of the barn before chucking it in the back of his truck.

Still feeling totally weak at the knees, I sorted out a clean pen for the ewe, added some hay and a bucket of water, then checked the rest before eventually settling her and her two lambs in their pen. I called in and thanked Elizabeth, saying I would be back along in a couple of hours before driving home.

Sitting on the bed I related all that had happened, brushing a tear from my cheek as emotions got the better of me.

"Come here," Aub leant forward to hug me. "I agree with Donald. You saved the ewe and two good lambs. You saw something most people wouldn't have noticed. A badly presented lamb stops a ewe opening up properly and can be really difficult to lamb. God you do smell! Go and wash and get changed!"

He pulled me forward and kissed me before pushing me away to the bathroom.

"We'll discuss any other problems when you're washed and clean!"

Our twenty ewes had produced thirty-nine live lambs, the only loss being the triplet from the ewe with the ring womb. Life went on but we wasted an awful lot of time watching the lambs gambol around the fields. This was what we wanted out of a farming life.

Chapter Eighteen

Changes

It was the hottest summer for quite a few years. I continued working with my beloved horses while Aub worked on the farm. Between us we managed our small flock, me learning so much every day.

One part I did struggle with was taking our first few lambs to the abattoir, situated on the Tewkesbury side of Cheltenham. My first delivery was just three big lambs ready to go, which I took down in the back of our old estate car of the time. Having delivered them I still remember having to pull over down a side road and crying my eyes out for having just done this to our lambs. I know we'd given them a wonderful life and I know all the arguments about there being no sheep in the fields if we didn't produce the lambs for meat, but none of these arguments would have stopped my sobbing. I hated it and told Aub I wouldn't take any more.

He didn't try to argue, just hugged me and arranged for lambs ready to go to be fitted in with Lower Througham's lambs on the lorry.

The following Autumn the old Suffolk ram performed again, but it was to be his last outing. We kept him in the little paddock with the ducks during the summer and after he had worked with the ewes. If I needed to cross the paddock he would charge at me causing actual bodily harm whenever he made contact. Aub only realised this when he commented on the old axe handle I had leaning up against the gate. I explained that it was my defence weapon against the ram and he just laughed and went out into the little paddock to see the ram, who flattened him. The following Monday he was on the lorry to Gloucester market!

Luckily the following year Aub was fit and healthy at lambing, although I did as much as him working in shifts. At the time, it was not general knowledge that pregnant women should not be working with sheep because of the risk of abortion. Luckily I was probably past the risk period, being six months pregnant with our daughter, my main problem being bending over lambing pens!

It doesn't really matter what time of year a farmer's wife has a baby, her husband is always going to be busy. Being a farmer having lambed endless sheep and calved many cows he had no desire to be there at the birth of our first child. Luckily Aub did manage to get me to Stroud maternity hospital in June, but having deposited me there rather failed to return and was quite surprised to discover I was hopefully, eventually, going to produce our child at Gloucester after complications set in.

Luckily all was well. I remember sitting on my bed in the ward waiting for his visit. I had made friends with Lucy in the next bed, who had also had a daughter and was delighted for her when her husband arrived carrying two dark red roses.

"One for each of my girls," he told her.

When Aub arrived he'd failed to buy flowers but did bring the bank statement, telling me I'd have to ring the manager because there was no money in our account and he needed to buy something for the sheep. He was amazed when I burst into tears and told him to do it himself. Once I'd gathered myself up, and Lucy had calmly told Aub it was probably hormones, I realised I would be the one speaking to the bank manager.

The only bright point of this being the manager was as amazed as me that I was having this conversation with him while in hospital, and assured me that he could arrange a small overdraft for the next couple of months. Hopefully we would soon sell some lambs and refill the coffers.

Love had obviously been in the air the previous year in Througham as Mary had also had a baby only three weeks before me. She visited me, saying she thought she was going to be late, having had to run for the bus. I was so relieved that a woman could run again only three weeks after having a baby that I gave her a great big hug.

Farming with a baby changes the complexion of everything you do. To begin with Aubrey had to combine his job and his sheep but later I found myself quite at home with our daughter strapped around in front of me while I tended to the animals every day needs. But life was beginning to see a change.

Lower Througham's owner died and his widow decided she would sell a major part of the farm, just keeping her main house at Sudgrove, with a cottage for Donald and Fiona, and a smaller acreage on that side of the valley. So Aubrey was looking for another job. Funnily enough one did materialise quite rapidly, but the new employer wanted me to look after his hunters as well, while Aub assisted his shepherd with a very large flock of sheep. This meant a move to Bampton, in Oxfordshire and nowhere for our own flock.

In fairness our 'flying flock' that should have produced lambs for us for one season had embraced their lifestyle in Gloucestershire and we sold them on as breeding ewes. It soon became apparent that life in Oxfordshire was not as appealing as Gloucestershire. For one thing it was flat. After the beautiful undulations of the Cotswold hills whatever beauty there was in the Oxfordshire villages it simply couldn't compare. I was also sad to leave our good friends in Througham, although Mary and Max left the hamlet about the same time as us, taking on a small farm in South Wales and we constantly kept in touch.

There was also the job situation. While there was an opening for an assistant shepherd the main requirement was for me to be a full-time groom for the owner's four hunters and several youngsters. Our daughter Heather could have been a complication but luckily our new house adjoined that of Bill the shepherd and his lovely wife Barbara, who took Heather into her kitchen every morning while I exercised horses and for a few more hours on hunting days if I was going out with hounds.

In the afternoons Heather was accustomed to being moved from one horse's manger to another while I groomed them or lying snugly wrapped up warm in the tack room while I cleaned the saddles and bridles. Aub's new job did offer him a vast experience with the flock of over 2000 ewes, but he felt our employer was not appreciative of the work done. It was nothing like working with Donald. Bill and Barbara made the job acceptable, but Aubrey was soon on the lookout for something else, and that would definitely be back in the Cotswolds.

One of Bill's main interests was sheep dog trialling and as Annie was becoming quite efficient round the sheep Bill suggested Aub might take her to a nursery trial to see how she got on. It was fairly local so Barbara and I decided we would arrive a little later than the men. In actual fact we arrived just before Annie's run. Aub sent her off on a right hand outrun to collect the sheep, which she did extremely well. However, from that point on things went pear shaped.

"Steady, steady. Lie down. LIE DOWN!" was all we could hear and then the six sheep, with Annie in hot pursuit appeared where the cars were parked, ran straight on through and off down the farm drive towards the town. By this time Aub had tried to disown his errant dog; the voice on the loudspeaker was thanking Mr Andrews but he was disqualified and other, more experienced dogs were sent off to overtake the sheep and hopefully bring them back to the field. This probably only took about three minutes before some very out of breath sheep were turned for home, but to Aub I think it seemed like a lifetime. In later discussions we felt Annie was happier just working at home.

We stayed in Oxfordshire until the end of the hunting season and lambing. Then the opportunity arose for Aub to work on the large estate we'd rented a cottage from when first married. It really was like coming home.

The new job had little to do with livestock though. Aub was now employed as a tractor driver involved with all the arable cultivations, so finding some land to restart our own flock was of major importance. This, however, was not as easy as it had been in Througham.

There was no one like Fred with land and buildings to make available to others and it was quite a struggle to find anything. We were lucky enough to be able to rent some old stables in the middle of the village, owned by the estate, and a couple of adjacent banky fields that were not of much use to anyone else, but this was wonderful for us.

All we needed now were the sheep. Even though Heather had now been joined by baby brother Mark, we had still managed to save most of the money from the sale of our original flock – certainly enough when the facilities we had available to us were not going to allow us to buy many more than ten or twelve ewes.

It was spring when we discovered that a farm close by was selling up their flock of North Country mules with lambs at foot, so this was our obvious destination one afternoon, with both children secured in the back of the car.

"If they're not too expensive we could maybe have fifteen ewes," Aub suggested hopefully.

When we arrived at the farm lambing was still ongoing, the shepherd looking fraught as most do at that time of the year. The yard we were led to held fourteen ewes all with white twin lambs at foot.

"These Texel crosses?" Aub asked.

"Yep. Good sorts aren't they?"

"Certainly are. Are your rams around here?" We were shown two large white rams, which were in actual fact 7/8ths Texel as the breed had not long been in the country and pure stock was still extremely expensive.

Considerable discussion followed, as is always the way with farmers and a price for the ewes and lambs was struck. We seemed to be parting with more money than I'd anticipated, but Aub assured me it was an excellent deal. With a borrowed land rover and trailer we would collect them the following day. That evening, with small children quiet in bed Aub was elated by his new purchases. In fact it was more a monologue than a conversation.

"Texels have only just come into this country. I'm sure they're going to be the sheep of the future. Did you see the shape of those lambs? The good top lines, the loin either side of the backbone. I know our old Suffolk ram did us quite well, but he was an expensive ram when Donald bought him and really looked the part, but his lambs never looked like these white ones."

"That's good then," I agreed. Even I could see how smart the lambs were.

"You know, I'm going to find out what they want for one of those rams if everything's going. We'll need a ram in the Autumn and I haven't seen any other Texel types around."

So that was how the flock evolved. The better of the two rams was also secured and our Texel cross flock had arrived.

With Aub working full time and me trying to look after sheep and two small children, lambing had to work around Aub's workload.

Our first lambs sold very well but I was still aware of the costs of feed for the animals was only just going to be covered by our sheep income, although Aub was quite happy to subsidise this with some of his wages. The ram ran with the ewes in September so we could lamb in February before he was tied up with Spring drilling, and all seemed fairly successful. Our ewes were prolific enough, although they would probably have had more lambs had we been able to leave lambing until March, but we were happy.

All that really didn't balance was the finances. For the small number of sheep we had, commercial lambs were never going to make us any money, and at this point they seemed to be costing us more than we had.

"We ought to breed some pedigree sheep," Aub announced one evening. "We're never going to make any money with commercials. We just haven't got the land."

"Mmm, so are we selling these and buying pedigree flock?"

"Oh, I wish. I want to go into Texels but they're an arm and a leg at the moment. Tell you what, let's put aside the harvest overtime money and see if we can buy a pedigree ewe this Autumn." He raised an eyebrow at me in question and foolishly I agreed. Aub could work very long hours during harvest but even so the extra money was not a huge amount, although often useful. Still, he was determined this would work and we could cope without the extra, so his plan unfolded.

The commercial lambs were well grown and sold well, the Mule ewes retained as most were only two or three years old, and Aub and I scoured the farming press for details of any Texel ewes for sale, but nothing appeared. We were very naïve and knew nothing of the newly formed Texel Sheep Society, nor had we come across any other farmers interested in the breed, the majority still favouring the black-faced Suffolks that had ruled supreme in British sheep breeding for many years.

Eventually we decided to put an advert in Farmer's Weekly looking for a Texel ewe for sale and waited with interest.

Chapter Nineteen

Texels and Tulip

It seemed a long time before there was any response to our advert, but I think the magazine had actually only been out for a couple of days when I received this reply.

"I gotta two-year old yow here. She's seven-eighths Texel an' she got two fine gimmer lambs on 'er by a Texel, so they're fifteen-sixteenths," the rasping male voice on the end of the phone told me. "Real good pair o' lambs they are. They'll grade no problem. £1500 the lot."

Thanks to Aubrey and a good deal of reading, I already knew that Pure Imported Texels were in such limited numbers, so graded up females sired by a pure Texel with a seven-eighths Texel mother were eligible for inspection to go into the flock book as a fifteen-sixteenths bred Texel.

"OK, thanks. I'll tell my husband when he gets in and if he's interested I'll get him to ring you."

"You won't find a better pair of gradin' up sheep anywhere."

"You say they're fifteen-sixteenths. What's the other sixteenth?" I asked, hoping I'd already asked all the right questions, although realising that if a Texel, even one to grade up, was going to cost this much we couldn't buy one.

"Gritstone, Derbyshire Gritstone."

"Oh, OK." I'd never heard of it.

This was my most exotic reply to date, but like two other responses I'd had earlier in the morning, so far away in the north of England that even if they fell within our price range, we would have to add the travel costs.

Once Aub had made the decision that he had to have a Texel, he was all guns blazing to get one. Having put aside all the harvest overtime, which looked like amounting to around £400, the thought that a ewe would be priced so far above that was sickening. Still, this was three sheep for £1500.

"A Derbyshire Gritstone is a big white woolly sheep with black and white speckles on its face and legs, something the Texel tries to avoid, so no I don't think so," were Aub's thoughts on my news when he appeared in that evening.

"I didn't know what he was talking about when he said a Gritstone. Mind you he was quite difficult to understand at all."

"That's typical of you. If the poor chap can't speak the Queen's English you can't understand him," he laughed, putting his hand over mine across the table.

"That's not fair. I just can't always understand a northern accent, just because you can."

"Don't worry darling, someone with a local accent will respond at some point. I hope," he added. "I was hoping someone would have something close by."

A couple of days later his prayers were answered. Tom Redman, a Texel breeder of some renown (we were later to discover), who lived a bare twenty miles away rang to offer us the choice of two Texel ewes.

Both were grading up sheep; one was a four year old ewe, being seven eighths Texel and other her two year old daughter, already graded. The older ewe was £300 and the younger one £350, so we arranged to go and see them on Saturday afternoon.

"We probably should go for the younger one," Aub suggested as we approached the farm. "I wonder if she lambed this year."

I felt I would just agree with him as my knowledge was so limited I was sure to say the wrong thing anyway.

The address was Newark Park and the palatial mansion in front of us was a little overpowering, but we were soon directed to a yard around the back that looked more in keeping with a farm. Concrete buildings and quite a lot of mud.

Here we were greeted by a jovial looking middle aged man and a younger version who had to be his son. We chatted for a short while, Aub explaining how impressed he'd been with the Texel cross lambs we'd had with the Mule ewes and how our small plot of land meant that if we were ever to make any money we'd have to look towards pedigree sheep.

Tom was really interested and helpful. He showed us two large sheep penned by the buildings, both square of stature, one with a broad forehead and the other with a narrower head. The broader headed ewe had big ears that folded across her brow and I fell for her immediately.

"This'ns Tulip, the older ewe," Tom told us, "and this one's her daughter."

"Tulip," I smiled. "I love her." Then remembered that I wasn't going to say anything.

"She's one of the first we had. Her breeding's French, but she came from Holland so we called her Tulip. And her ears make her look a bit like a Tulip," said the younger man.

"What d'you think?" Aub asked me. "I like Tulip best. Not so keen on the head on the younger one." So it was agreed.

"If she's your only one you'd better leave her here to run with my good tup then," Tom said. To be honest I don't think either if us had thought that far ahead, but were very grateful when Tom offered to put her in lamb to a top French Texel ram he had just purchased, Newark Hors d'oeuvre.

I knew we were naïve, but little did we realise how lucky we were to have come across someone as honest and helpful as Tom, and this was the start of a lifelong friendship.

Tulip was apparently from the renowned Jacques Pelzer line and Hors D'ouvres the equally good Prevost line, so as far as a foundation ewe for a pedigree flock we couldn't have done better. This really was the start of a pedigree flock for us, because Tom took Tulip back to his ram for the next two years until we could afford to buy an unrelated ram lamb from him, and Tulip left us ewe lambs every year but one, when she had one ram lamb and one ewe lamb.

Chapter Twenty

Bulb

When Tulip lambed we were totally traumatised, as was she I'm sure. Lambing Tulip for the first time taught us one very good lesson that we have never forgotten. A Texel does not need as much food as a Mule, especially when she's having a single – although as we didn't scan in those days, we weren't to know until we saw two feet that would have done a Shire horse proud.

I'd been watching her for days and the only plus point I could think of, although it was a major plus, was that Aub was close by, so came rapidly when I contacted him. She also decided to lamb during the afternoon rather than in the middle of the night!

We had been very lucky earlier in the year to rent a small barn and seven acres from a local farmer, who had kept a couple of cows. I just happened to see him the day he had sent his cows to market, so asked him what he was going to be doing with the land and within a few minutes had secured the rental. The little barn was really just a lean to, but it was built of Cotswold stone and the roof was fairly waterproof, so we were over the moon at this acquisition. Only a quarter of a mile from home it suited us ideally and was housing the remaining Mules still to lamb and Tulip.

You could have heard a pin drop in the barn as Aub worked away gently massaging and lubricating inside the ewe and around the feet of this enormous lamb. This was when he discovered that a plastic coated loop of wire was the best lambing aid we would ever find, as there was no way that a hand could go into the birthing canal as well as the head come out. I sat against Tulip's shoulder, stroking her, holding my breath for what seemed to be forever.

"Crikey darling, you've had far too many biscuits, haven't you," Aub told her, trying to lighten the situation. He sat back exhausted, rubbing his hand where he'd been struggling to gain some movement in the pelvis.

"At least it's coming the right way," I said, wishing there was more I could do.

"We'd never get it if it wasn't," Aub muttered. These days, for a lamb this size, we would discuss having a vet out for a caesarean.

"Can I help at all?"

"You can have a go at opening her up a bit. Your hands are smaller than mine so it may help. Use plenty of slipjel though."

We swapped ends and I undertook the arduous task of slipping my hand inside the ewe, covering the two feet that kept appearing with lubricant and gently opening the ewe's cervix so at last I could feel a nose. Now it was my hand being squashed by her pelvis when Tulip pushed. We swapped back and Aub worked away, gradually being able to slip the wire loop over the lambs head and lambing ropes on both feet, although that's never as easy as it sounds as they always start to pull their legs back inside the ewe and the ropes often slip off if you dare to relax them a centimetre.

"I don't think we're going to get this alive." Aub was by now manoeuvring the legs so one was forward more than the other so the lamb didn't jam on the shoulders.

"Oh we must. Come on Tulip, push."

And she did. Steadily, with both of us on a lambing rope, Aub also guiding the head with his wire and dear old Tulip trying hard she eventually pushed out the most massive lamb we'd ever seen. As we gently pulled the lamb out of the ewe, its body seemed to go on forever.

Then, to our utter amazement, it shook its head and looked us straight in the eye, then baa'd. We could both have cried, and I probably did, but Aub rapidly rubbed the lamb with straw and passed it forward for Tulip to lick, having been delighted to check it was a ewe lamb.

"That has to be the biggest lamb I've ever seen," he said. "I'll get the hanging scale and when Tulip's washed her a bit we'll weigh her."

When we did, the lamb weighed almost eighteen pounds. We christened her Bulb, mainly due to her bulbous shape! Quite understandably she took a while to stand, but Tulip ensured she sucked as soon as she'd finished washing her, by simply standing over her and Bulb raising her head to the teat, she was so big. Little were we to know that the fact that Tulip was happy to do this would be the life saver for her daughter.

We gave Tulip a bucket of water and left mother and daughter alone for a while, although didn't venture far away. I boiled the kettle that we kept precariously on a small table at the end of the barn and made cups of coffee, a sure way to bring Aub round. I knew he was both physically and mentally exhausted. Our Texel flock had stumbled at its first hurdle, but hopefully recovered.

Sadly, over the next few days I realised all was not completely well with Bulb. She struggled to stand up and although we'd initially put this down to soreness, she should have been over that by now. Tulip was luckily thriving, producing as much milk as a dairy cow, which was not helping matters as Bulb was almost growing before our eyes. Having administered basic antibiotics and painkillers following her birth, by day two I rang our vet, John, who although he'd trained with farm animals, now really specialised in horses. A man who certainly never suffers fools, known by some of his clients and many of the staff as 'God', he has always done great work for us. Walking into the barn he smiled.

"It's actually good to occasionally come back to grass roots farming stock," he said. "Have to say I'm amazed you got this out alive, especially without damaging the ewe, it's enormous."

"Well she has grown a bit since birth but she was eighteen pounds."

"I can believe it. But something's not right is it?"

John helped the huge lamb up and tried to get her to stand, but her legs simple seemed to buckle under her.

"Has she stood up at all?" he asked. "How old is she?"

"Oh yes. It took her a while to stand, but we just thought she was sore, and I still think that was the case, but once she was up she was following the ewe about quite normally. She's three days old, but it was only yesterday evening that she seemed to struggle to stand and when she did, she felt really solid and preferred to move backwards rather than forwards, but after a couple of steps just fell down again."

"Well she's obviously suckling," he said, "and she looks bright enough in herself."

"The ewe's wonderful. She just stands over her and the lamb's so big she simply has to raise her head."

"Well, I have to admit I don't know what the problem is. I've never seen anything like this before, but I'll try to find out. I know a very good sheep vet. I'll ring him and ask his thoughts. Only other option might be to pop her down to Elmbridge Court, to the VI (veterinary investigation) centre. The boffins down there might have a clue."

This was how the following afternoon I was parading Bulb on a concrete path before two white-coated gentlemen, both scratching their heads. Having bundled her in the back of our old Maxi on a blanket, with Aub's help and much to Tulip's disgust, it took two of us to unload her on the grass verge. Surprisingly Bulb actually staggered to her feet for a few backward strides before lying down on the path staring at us.

"Well, I really don't know what the problem is," said one of the men. "Only thing I can suggest is we do a PM on her."

"She's not going to die," I probably almost shouted at him, but was grateful for his help to lift her back onto her blanket in the boot of the car. It's so annoying that tears can flood out to display anger, but I was furious that this man couldn't understand the passion we had to make this work.

Back at home I started to lose faith. Aub and I spent as much time as possible with Tulip and her child, obviously unable to let them outside for more than a short time during the day when the weather was good. Finally came the morning when I found Bulb on her side, obviously in pain, legs outstretched with a fit of cramp. I rang John straight away and told him the situation and asked him to come and put her down. Nothing we were trying was working and his sheep vet hadn't come up with any ideas either.

"I'll be with you in about half an hour, but don't give up. I'll give Terry a ring before I come."

John drove into the yard actually smiling rather than looking grim at failure.

"It's selenium deficiency. I'm pretty sure it's selenium deficiency. Cramp is the most obvious sign and that was what gave Terry the clue. It's been seen in fast growing Charolais calves since their import into this country. He's not seen it in sheep before, but I've got something to give her and we'll just wait and see."

John gave Bulb an injection and a muscle relaxant, probably dystocel and finadyne, and then suggested we went back to the house for a cup of tea. Aub was at work and we had no mobiles so I had to wait till he returned to tell him the news. When John and I went back to the farm Bulb was standing and soon was walking around. The injection of selenium had worked that quickly.

While we've never had another lamb of the size of Bulb, nor one that has grown as fast as she has, we have had quite a bit of trouble with selenium deficiency, or white muscle disease as it's also known. We solve it now with trace element and vitamin drenches, but I have always been amazed at the speed this can be resolved if it occurs by either administering a drench or injection plus pain killer.

After thanking John and making sure he passed our gratitude on to Terry, I took great satisfaction in ringing the VI centre and telling them the lamb was now skipping round the barn and what the solution had been. Hopefully it enlightened them should anyone else have a lamb or calf in that situation.

Bulb's troubled start may well have caused permanent damage as although she went on to increase our Texel flock alongside her

Sue on
The Squire

Aubrey with
his father and
their sheepdog
Laddie

Above: In the thick of things. Motorcycle football

Left: Aubrey and Sue in Througham

Windmill Cottage

The notorious
Satan

Aub and Gustav

Nell, one of the best. Immortalised by Mary Griese
under the title Brains and Beauty

Aubrey giving Heather and Mark a trial run before the parties

Annie proving how versatile a sheepdog can be

Party in full swing

Texel ewe and lambs

Blue Texel lambs

Swincombe Double Scotch winning the Supreme Championship
at the Builth NSA Ram Sale

Miserden Shearling Ewe sold at English National Sale Worcester

Miserden Klinker, our first Blue Texel ram
lamb winning at the Royal Show

Tsurcana sheep and shepherd in Romania

Aubrey judging Masham Sheep Fair

Sue with Supreme Champion Blue Texel at Builth NSA Ram Sale

Texel Rams being loaded onto RMS St Helena, food
supplies going with them

Texels arriving in United Arab Emirates

Beast from the East. Snow blocking the field gates

Jill and Maisie

Sue and Aubrey with Jill and Maisie in 2019

mother, bringing with her outstanding breed lines, her lifespan was only that of five or six years, while Tulip was with us until she was fourteen, still producing lambs at eleven.

Chapter Twenty-One

Buying a Ram

Tom was true to his word and kindly took Tulip back each year to go to the ram, but eventually we thought we should purchase a ram lamb of our own.

As Aub was working, I was sent to Gloucester market where the Gloucester and Border Counties Texel Breeders were having a sale as part of Barton Fair. As usual funds weren't flush, in fact I was quite sure our bank manager would be horrified if he knew the intent of my journey, but we felt we couldn't go on taking Tom's goodwill for granted.

I'd been to markets with Aub, but looking round the pens on my own was daunting and I was glad to see in the catalogue Tom had several ram lambs entered. Having tracked him down he was happy to show me his stock, emphasising that the biggest of the three lambs in his pen was the obvious choice.

"Breeding you won't find anywhere else," he assured me. "Look, good strong lamb. Make you an ideal stock tup."

He left me studying the lamb and carried on discussing it with other potential buyers.

Before the sale, a show for sale entries was being held in a small concrete area close to the pens. There were classes for shearling rams, ram lambs and shearling ewes and the stock forward looked impressive. I joined the crowd of people around the makeshift ring and watched with interest as the winning shearling ram was selected. He looked strong and powerful, the audience of farmers around the ring appearing to agree with the judge. But it was the lambs I was most interested in as Tom was showing his big lamb.

The ring had seemed full just now with the shearlings, but now there were even more ram lambs, all well grown and to my uneducated eye, most looking fairly similar. As I watched I noticed some stood four square better than others unless their handler pushed and pulled them into a good position. Tom's really caught my eye as he stood correctly all the time, looking smart and alert and interested in the proceedings.

The judge walked along the front of the row of lambs looking at their heads, the set of their ears and their facial colour, preference being given to those with black tear ducts and noses on their snow-white faces. He walked along the back of the line, looking at the way they stood, looking for correct feet and pasterns. He handled each sheep, from their mouths, checking the teeth were correct, something of great importance if the sheep is to have a long grazing life, through their backs, hands spread feeling for muscle, then the backend. As he handled a lamb he liked, he told the handler to take him forward and soon he had a shorter front row of his preferred lambs, which included Tom's. Those remaining in the back line were let loose so the judge could check he hadn't missed a good lamb that caught his eye when running free, but decided not, so those were returned to their pens.

Next the judge loosed the front line of lambs and stood well back to watch the way they moved and stood naturally, without anyone holding them and correcting their position.

After what seemed an age he started to pull out the lambs he liked in order, with Tom's lamb being first. I was delighted and horrified. Delighted because to me he looked by far the best lamb there, but horrified that he had now risen far beyond my chances of buying him. He was awarded first prize lamb and reserve Champion overall, creating a lot of interest in Tom's pen between show and sale time.

Realising that I wouldn't have the money to buy Tom's lamb I looked through other pens of lambs and shearlings, noting two or three in each section that I liked. I was beginning to understand some of Aub's requirements from a sheep, but also the pressure on me to select something he'd like. First and foremost it had to have a good top line, a straight line from the neck to the tail, with no dip behind the shoulders as some had.

"Needs a good loin," he'd said, although to be honest he hadn't been much help, simply saying I knew enough about conformation to make a sensible choice! Hopefully I did.

The shearling rams were first in the sale ring. The main assembly of commercial farmers were looking for a strong ram they could turn out with 50 – 60 ewes and find themselves with a crop of good strong lambs the following Spring. Prices started to fly, the first two I'd selected as possibles went over my budget before I had chance to put a bid in. This was getting depressing. While I knew the bank manager would have a fit at me spending anything, I had set my limit at £300, but most seemed to be making 400 – 500 guineas and there was no way I could pay a cheque for that without it bouncing!

The last of my selection of the shearlings entered the ring to a real buzz and topped the days prices so far. I could congratulate myself that my choice of rams coincided with other farmers. Perhaps I was beginning to know what I should look for.

Next came the ram lambs and I'd decided to wait until Tom's lambs had been through before bidding on anyone else's just in case no one else wanted his first prize lamb, but of course that didn't happen. He stood in the ring looking every bit a Champion and his price rose to the eventual finale at 800gns.

Tom's next ram lamb, almost as big and impressive as the first, was not much sought after but did go on to make over 400gns. His final lamb, a twin to his winner I realised when I glanced again at the catalogue, was much smaller than anything that had so far been through the ring, although he did have the required good top line and a smart head just like his brother. Due to his lack of size bidding was sticky. Would he cope with our ewes? There was Tulip and four of her daughters now. Not a huge task for a lamb but would he be able to reach them? I put my hand up as the auctioneer asked for 150gns. He looked at me, as a new bidder not sure if I'd waved by mistake, but I nodded and he took my bid.

There was a period of uncertainty while he sought a further price rise, then another agreed to 180gns, at which point Tom pointed out that this was a full brother to his reserve Champion and worth far more and the auctioneer let the lamb out of the ring and back to his pen before I'd gathered myself up with a further bid.

Being my first time bidding at an auction I'd rather lost my bottle, so three or four lambs went through before I gathered myself up and bid again at another I'd quite liked. However, so had several others and his price soon rose well beyond my limit. Eventually I wandered off back towards the pens, where I bumped into Tom heading for the café.

"You bought anything then?" he asked.

"No, failed completely. I'll have to go now. Got to pick the children up. I did try to buy your little one. Have you sold him?"

"D'you like him? He's small but he's well bred. Twin to that good one. You can have him for 180 if you want him."

Tom turned round and we walked back to his pen. The lamb looked smaller by the minute but there was something about him I liked.

"You look after him and he'll do you OK. You've only a few ewes for him."

"Will he be big enough, will he reach?"

"He'll manage. If you want him just go to the office and tell them," and he strode off back towards the café.

Glancing at my watch I realised I'd have to hurry, so clutching my bag I ran over to the office and wrote out a cheque for £189, (the sheep were all sold in guineas), praying it would go through when tried, but also knowing I would have the lamb home well before then. Luckily I found someone who helped me lift the little guy into the back of the old pickup and drove home in a mixture of euphoria having purchased him and fear my purchase might not be what Aub had been expecting.

I met up with him outside the village shop, where he was probably buying tobacco, when I called at the school next door to pick up the children.

"How on earth's he going to work? He's half the size of the ewes. Couldn't you have bought anything bigger?" Both children thought the lamb looked lovely and very cuddly and he attracted a lot of attention from their friends.

"He's got another month to grow on before we use him," I said. "You should have taken the day off and come and bought one. We've got no money and yet I'm meant to buy the best sheep at the sale. His full brother was first prize ram lamb and reserve champion so we've got some good bloodlines."

The little guy looked around him, unaware of the unpleasant remarks, and I drove off to settle him in a stable and take the children home for tea. When I told Aub his new ram was carrying on the flower names with 'Newark Larkspur' he scathingly said it was totally effeminate and probably suited him.

Sadly, all did not go well initially with Larkspur as he soon showed signs of pneumonia. I called the vet out, not risking my large investment to our limited medical knowledge. Although I had several sleepless nights assuming he'd die, with prompt and correct medical treatment he made a full recovery. He also increased slightly in size due to my indulgent feeding before his mating challenge, which he completed with no problem. The ewes seemed quite enamoured with the handsome guy. Over that winter he grew on to become a very handsome shearling and matured into a superb animal, producing some excellent quality lambs over a number of years.

I discovered that his brother had been sold to a top breeder, and their Midhill and Annan parentage had given us some very elite breeding. As with everything we had from Tom, this lamb proved to be very genuine.

We purchased another ram from Tom some years later, this time with Aub coming to the sale and making the selection. Newark Prince, a shearling by Cambwell King was another well bred tup, yet when we got him home, we were both disappointed with him.

"He looked better than this at the sale. He's got no head and wouldn't be the strongest behind the shoulder. Can't think why I bought him," and off he went muttering while I went home to make a cup of tea. Then the phone rang.

"It's Roger from Bruton Knowles," I shouted as he came in the door. "He thinks we've got the wrong ram."

It materialised that while I was paying in the office, a friend had helped Aub manoeuvre and load the ram and Aub hadn't checked the ear tag, because he was sure they had grabbed the right one. Well he hadn't. Luckily the purchaser of the ram that now stood in our stable had checked the tag when his had arrived home.

This brought on a new panic as we were now blood testing for Maedi Visna, a serious debilitating disease that was starting to be recognised. Although all the sheep at the sale were of that health status, the commercial farm where our ram had gone probably wouldn't be. Aub immediately loaded the ram into the back of the pickup and drove off to the Forest of Dean where the other purchaser lived, while I rang Roger to confirm what we were doing. When he returned with his correct ram Aub was all smiles and when he unloaded Prince I could see why. He was of a far superior stamp and I could see he was the one we'd selected.

"We were jolly lucky the other chap rang Roger, 'cos you still hadn't noticed yours had the wrong ear tag. If we hadn't been so quick he could have turned this one out with his ewes. What did the bloke say when he saw his own ram?"

"He didn't seem too perturbed, just pleased we ran his back for him. I was so relieved when I saw this one. Luckily he still had him separate in a stable so it was easy to swap and I shot off.

In future we always made sure we checked the tag number!

Chapter Twenty-Two

Showing

Gradually as time went by, we were able to rent more patches of grassland, often quite a long way away from home, that we could graze for part of the year. Very little was ideal, since it only became available because no one else wanted it, often because it needed fencing; so we became dab hands at electric fencing.

We purchased four more Texel ewes locally, bringing our flock total to seven ewes and two ewe lambs, who wouldn't be bred from until they were yearlings. We still had some Mules, but gradually we were becoming a pedigree flock, and Tulip was continuing to consistently breed us females. Once you get to seven ewes, production really does increase and the flock swelled. In the next couple of years the Mules were replaced by Texels and we started selling rams at the local markets. This was when we realised how much of a struggle it was going to be to convert local farmers from their traditional Suffolk rams to trying a Texel, even though Texel cross lambs were now topping the lamb trade.

We also ventured into the show ring.

By now Tulip had surpassed herself by producing twin females almost every year. We'd kept up with the flower names for the lambs after Bulb, so gradually we had Snowdrop and Celandine, Daisy and Buttercup, Daffodil and Narcissus the one year she produced one ewe and one ram lamb and Rosy and Posy! Snowdrop was a lovely lamb and grew into a beautiful gimmer, who we showed with great success at a small show locally. Then we decided we might venture into deeper waters.

Our main local show is Three Counties, which was quite a big step for us to take, but we looked long and hard at our sheep, admired our shearling rams that looked fit and well and, along with a couple of lambs, entered these at the prestigious show.

The show at Malvern runs for three days, but is close enough for us to return home each night, which is what we did then. At that time the show was held during the week so on the Monday we loaded up sheep and children and headed for the Malverns.

Sadly, we were aware once we arrived that our stunning rams were nowhere near good enough for the show, but we took them out in the ring on the Tuesday, to be last in the class. Our fit and healthy rams looked half-starved compared to the enormous animals in the ring and we felt totally embarrassed. However, the other competitors made us feel welcomed and overall we were pleased we'd gone. One old farmer came up to me as I was looking at the superb prizewinning sheep in his pen and gave me the best piece of advice anyone can have from the show world.

"Nothing wrong with your sheep. Just get a bigger bucket!" His advice to feed show sheep far more than we ever thought they could eat was sound advice and the following year we appeared at the show with animals fit to compete against anyone.

Juggling sheep, children and Aub's work was an art form. To make any money we needed to sell our sheep at the sales and the saying that you need to be in something for ten years before you're accepted certainly rings true with pedigree breeding. In fact, it's probably twenty years. Most things in farming require you to have been there for a generation!

To sell at the sales we had to be seen around, and to sell at the Welsh sales, where Texel rams were welcomed, we needed to show at the Royal Welsh Show and the sheep needed to be good. Part of their popularity in Wales came when Defra, or MAFF as they were then known, were giving headage payments for sheep, hill sheep having greater value than lowland. Using a white faced Texel ram it was possible to breed a better quality lamb while still convincing any inspectors that it was just a Welsh hill sheep, whereas with a Suffolk cross the colouring gave it away.

Our show competitors were selected, moved to a better field and fed twice a day until they looked incredibly fat. About a week before the show they were caught up, their faces and legs washed and their bodies were sprayed with a strange colour mixture, that once dried should come out a biscuit colour.

Our first attempt at colouring was both amusing and horrifying. Being sensible we decided to spray some non-competitors first.

After we'd sprayed them, Aub varying the strength slightly as we went through them, they were turned in the paddock so they could dry in the sun, while we did something else.

"Have a look and see if the colours OK," said Aub a little later.

"What colour do you want them?" I asked, standing on the wall looking at the motley crew in the field.

"Well, you know. Sort of biscuit colour."

"Hmm, well we've got a couple of digestives, two custard creams, three gingernuts and a Bourbon."

Aub eventually sorted out the strength needed to gain a

digestive biscuit colour which satisfied him.

Aub's work commitments in late July meant that showing at the Royal Welsh fell to me, and as the years progressed the start of the holidays luckily meant the children could come with me. By now we had a number of good friends in the Texel breed and showing was a fun combination of a camping holiday and serious competition. Once the sheep were settled in their pens, fed and watered, we would park on top of the hill overlooking the showground, muck out the trailer and lay out sleeping bags. A makeshift plastic awning would run from the car to the trailer, and basic cooking facilities were organised and tents erected for the children.

Once again we caught up with our friend Mary, who always has a stand in the Glamorgan Hall. She was displaying her wonderful paintings under her heading Slightly Sheepish, although she painted all farm animals not simply sheep. The part of the hill allocated to car and trailer parking was on a slope, and one year this was so noticeable I had to tie a piece of baler twine to the top side of the trailer then round Mary to stop her rolling over onto me in the night.

With her children, Cassie and Rohan, we would have great fun in the evening, but often left all the children to continue sleeping the following morning when Mary and I went down the hill to our pens and stand. The show ran for four days so after the competitions there was plenty of time to watch cattle and ponies showing.

To begin with show ring success was not easy, and sometimes disappointment was bitter. Early on in our showing career we bred a lovely shearling ewe, Biggles, who had already won several shows, including Reserve Champion at the Bath and West, but was completely overlooked by the judge at the Welsh. The classes were big, sixty or seventy sheep in one class not being unusual, and Biggles had been thrown out on the first draw. Later that day the judge was walking down the lines, talking to competitors, both successful and not, so I asked him what he'd disliked about my ewe.

Climbing into her pen he handled her and denied having sent her out straight away, saying what a lovely sheep she was. To my delight Biggles backed up to him, lifted her tail and peed down his immaculate cavalry twill trousers. I felt she expressed herself well.

After the first day's showing the children and I would spend the next three days wandering round the vast showground, looking at other livestock and country pursuits, often partying late into the night.

Five days at a show without Aubrey's help was incredibly tiring, though, and although I coped for several years, the time I fell asleep for a split second while driving home to suddenly find myself on the wrong side of the road, I decided was the last. We revisited the show in later years when Aubrey was able to come as well.

Chapter Twenty-Three

Our Own Farm Tenancy

A chance conversation with Donald and Fiona, who we were still in touch with, led to our greatest farming achievement so far. Donald was due to retire after a deterioration in his health meant he could no longer carry on the farm work, and his employer decided to let the farm.

The acreage was smaller now, since the Througham land where Aubrey had worked had been sold on the death of his employer's husband, but it was still more than we could afford. However, the layout made it possible for us to rent the grassland banks while another local farmer took over the eighty acres of arable land.

We were also lucky that Donald, who had become a little cantankerous in his old age, was still going to live in the farmhouse, and was probably going to be around the farm, so the owner wanted someone who could get along with him to take over the tenancy. We were lucky enough to fit the bill.

Aub and I were actually rather pleased that Donald and Fiona were going to continue living there. As we couldn't live on site it was good to have someone we trusted nearby, and I was hopeful Donald would assist or at least advise if I had any lambing problems when Aub was not around. Aub was working full time and although he tried to time a holiday with our lambing, things never seemed to quite go to plan.

For us it was heaven. For the first time, all the sheep would be contained within one boundary fence, with a building we could use as a sheep shed. Again, finances had to be discussed, because the rent was far more than we had been paying. But we both agreed that we could afford this new venture if we cashed in the small endowment policy we had taken out some years previously.

As Aub pointed out, we'd taken it out as security for the future, and this was our future. It was the best decision we could have made.

We now had a pedigree flock of over forty texels, but with more grazing we would be able to keep our female lambs and bring them into the flock as breeding ewes and increase the flock size. Any ungrazed grassland we cut as hay.

With Aub working full time, lambing had to be organised around his arable responsibilities, when he could take a week's holiday. To avoid clashing with Spring drilling we moved lambing forward to the middle of February. Not always the best of weather, nor the most productive as our ewes would produce more lambs later in their breeding season, but it worked.

Luckily, for a number of years, with small numbers, I'd managed any that lambed before Aub's week off. By now I had become reasonably competent at lambing a sheep, and really quite good at keeping lambs alive. A definite bonus. But now that our flock size had increased, I assured him that I really did need assistance. and for longer than he would be able to give me around his own work commitments.

Mary was now living close by. Her marriage to Max had

disintegrated several years previously and she had moved back to Gloucestershire. She was happy to come and help, and most importantly she was fairly negotiable on wages. Obviously she couldn't work for us for nothing, but looking back, she virtually did. In all honesty, her assistance and sense of humour was sometimes all that kept me sane.

Some nights she would stay and others she'd go home, sometimes quite early in the afternoon as she still had her own arrangements and engagements to sort out. By now she was running both art and writing classes. Evenings and nights weren't too bad as Aub was always around, although he appreciated getting some sleep as he'd have a full day at work the following day.

Together Mary and I would work through everything that needed doing, from feeding ewes, checking ewes and lambs in pens, those in bigger pens and those outside. We bottled lambs, humped hay and straw around, bedded up and periodically lambed a ewe or at least moved one with her lambs to an individual pen if she'd been helpful and lambed on her own.

There were times when we were so tired we could hardly communicate. It was an unwritten agreement that we'd only say one F word daily, although later in lambing this was not always adhered to. (We'd never used that word until our children's generation seemed to find it commonplace, and still felt it should be kept for dire situations!)

One of the further barns we were using, where we would run six or seven ewes with their lambs if the weather was too bad to turn out, had a huge muddy puddle verging on being a lake in front of it. To make light of the situation, we named one barn Lanzarote and another Tenerife, suggesting it would be good if lambs didn't fall in the swimming pool en route to their resort.

This drove Aub insane when I tried to explain where certain sheep were, and great amusement to the vet one day when I asked him to look at a lamb in Lanzarote. He'd always thought I was a mad, now he was sure.

As we weren't living on the farm, although we had a shed to make tea and coffee and raid the biscuit box, it was wonderful to actually return to a warm house occasionally. One of us would cast an eye round the sheep shed and suggest nothing looked likely to die if we went home for a couple of hours during the middle of the day, but we always had to set an alarm clock, or we could have slept in the armchairs in front of the fire until Aub came home. Some days we did oversleep and arrived back at the farm in panic to find two or three ewes had lambed while we'd been gone, but we never admitted that to Aub.

As lambing progressed we could be climbing over pens to get to further makeshift accommodation, when more ewes lambed at once than we had room for. To save the endless trek from the sheep shed to the middle yard for the medicine box, I'd put an old table at one end of the shed and brought the medicine box in there. It was here, under this table, I found Mary grovelling on her knees, building a straw bed for a wayward bottle lamb we had no spare pen to house.

"Look, I've made her a nest." She proudly showed me this huge circular nest of straw housing one small orphan lamb.

"That's not a nest, it's a bloody erie!"

Needless to say the lamb was christened Eagle and should definitely have gone for meat, but no, she stayed as a totally useless breeding ewe for a number of years. Whether it simply is that bottle reared lambs have little maternal instinct because they've been reared artificially I don't know, but I do try to make sure they don't progress into the flock these days.

We still seemed so short of money.

"Why?" Aub would ask me.

"Because the blasted sheep cost so much to keep. Look at the accounts. It's all spent on them. The only new thing I've bought to wear for the past five years is been a new pair of wellies. I'm hardly squandering the profits."

This did little to placate him, but he did take on board my comments and we did our best to cut our costs: studying the monthly outlay and trying hard to improve on it. Vet's bills were extortionate and we had tried to treat as much ourselves as possible. Feed bills were probably higher than some farmers, but ours was the equivalent of a hill farm, over 900ft up on an exposed escarpment, where grass came later than it did on lower lying farms, so we fed both concentrates and hay far later than other breeders.

To be honest, we were trying to breed pedigree sheep in hardier conditions than most and eventually this was to be part of our success. Once we started to establish ourselves with customers, we found it easy to get repeat orders for rams, mainly because other rams these farmers had bought would melt away, having been stuffed with feed, once they ran them commercially. Our great selling point was, and still is, our sheep are reared commercially, living outside on exposed hillsides in all weathers and usually when they are sold, they find themselves with a slightly softer climate and continue to grow on.

However, in the meanwhile, as well as struggling with farm finances, we also had two children who wanted to retain a certain standard of living and be able to entertain their friends. Luckily, they soon realised that our house and farm was the most popular venue for friends, and I rarely found the house empty of children. In fact, I sometimes had to suggest they might like a lift home or stay the night.

Both Heather and Mark had ponies, usually borrowed rather than bought, we had dogs, cats and chickens and plenty of lambs and our lifestyle was a chaotic novelty to many. As were the children's birthday parties. I'm still amazed when we bump into some of their friends in the village, now parents themselves, who openly say that our birthday parties were the best they went to.

While our children could come back from a friend's party telling me about the magic show parents had organise, or been on a swimming party with pizza and chips supplied for twenty children, I felt our cheap parties would be a sad disappointment, but this was never the case. I always made sure there was plenty of home cooked food and homemade ginger beer, usually served picnic style in the garden as both children conveniently had birthdays in the middle of the summer. I made cakes to suit the child, making Mark tractors and space ships and Heather, My Little Pony castles and one year a chocolate covered pony.

Having cut out a shape and iced it, using chocolate covered swiss rolls for its legs, I decorated the board with green iced grass and yellow icing buttercups. I had some yellow icing left so I decided to liven up the chocolate legs with yellow spots and felt quite proud of my creation until Aub put his head round the kitchen door and asked if the pony had bots.

He was the star of these parties, with an ancient wire sheep trailer attached to the back of his scramble bike. The field behind our house had a number of undulating mounds through it, and once we'd piled all the children in the trailer (with numbers exceeding space but somehow we got them all in, possibly with the birthday child riding astride the bike on Aub's lap), he then took off round the field at great speed, giving a ride to far outweigh Alton Towers. Health and Safety would have had a fit, but those parties stayed in all those children's memories through to today.

During the school holidays both children, plus hangers on, made full use of the wonderful parkland adjacent to our house. This was an area where children could run wild, climb trees, paddle in the fords and learn to gallop around and jump logs on their long-suffering ponies. Most of their friends learnt to ride and in return their parents took ours to the cinema and swimming.

On one occasion at Three Counties show I remember having four pens of sheep plus another of small children sitting on bales, happily sucking ice lollies while I sorted the sheep out. Our life was a great experience for them.

Chapter Twenty-Four

Scotch

Once again I was sent off to buy a stock ram, this time to the English National Texel sale, then held in marquees on Three Counties showground at Malvern and with a little more money in my pocket.

Going to sales alone now was nowhere near as daunting as my first escapade buying Larkspur as I knew far more breeders and had many friends in the Texel breed. I also knew enough now to know what I liked, although that didn't always correspond with what Aub liked.

Having studied the catalogue I was searching for my perfect ram and had marked several to look at in the pens before they went through the ring. There were some good lambs at this sale and I was sure I'd find one that would suit us, but as the sale progressed all those I had selected soared to high prices, many being bought by syndicates of breeders whose combined buying power took the prices far beyond my limit.

Wandering back to the pens for a further look at lambs later in the sale I bumped into a breeder I knew and went with him to his pen. The lamb I'd marked in my catalogue wasn't there, but when questioned his breeder muttered that he'd been thrown out by the inspector, for no good reason. Sadly this could often happen. If the inspector was Scottish he often looked on his fellow countrymen's sheep more favourably than the English and Welsh bred, and knowing this, having questioned further, I followed my friend to his trailer, where he'd put the rejected lamb.

He was all I could have asked for, and I could certainly see why his breeder was sore at the rejection. He ran the lamb out into a pen so I could handle him and see him move. He handled like a brick, with muscle running the full length of his loin and gigot. He was alert and smart and probably completely out of my price range, but he'd been rejected for being weak on a back leg.

"He's travelled a long way and he'd just got off the trailer," he explained. "He'll be fine."

In fairness I couldn't see a lot wrong with the leg, except possibly the amount of weight and muscle the lamb was carrying could put a bit of strain on his legs, something often seen in the well pushed sale lambs. I had to have him, but sensibly showed a bit of caution.

"He is nice, but he could have a bit of a weakness there, couldn't he?"

"He's a smart lamb. He'd have won in the show and everything. He's for sale."

We negotiated and the lamb moved into our trailer.

There was a certain amount of apprehension and excitement when I arrived home. Aub had finished work and was waiting at the farm to see our new purchase.

"Not huge is he?"

To be honest I'd never expected great praise for my purchase, but I was there to defend him.

"You put a hand on him. He handles like a brick."

"Hmm, what d'yer pay for him?"

Aub was impressed when I told him, but I knew I'd have to admit he'd been thrown out at the inspection. He made the lamb move round the stable.

"Doesn't look too bad to me. We'll cut his food down, take some of the weight of his legs and run him with the others. See how he goes."

Swincombe Double Scotch sired us a number of excellent lambs, but never really grew to the size Aub wanted. We used him as a lamb, when he left us some really solid children, but the following year, after using him again on a few early ewes I agreed we'd take him as part of our consignment to the Builth NSA sale the following September.

The National Sheep Association ram sale at Builth Wells is a spectacle to behold. There are sheds and marquees full of every breed of sheep found in this country and some interesting crossbreeds. By now Texels had become a leading light in terminal sires, surpassing the reigning Suffolks, and there was an entry of over 2000 Texel rams for sale. The afternoon prior to the sale sees all breeds holding their own shows, an important highlight of the sale, each vendor able to show one animal in each category, shearling ram, ram lamb, shearling ewe and ewe lamb, with an overall Champion being selected from the winners. Often the majority of the spectators are other breeders looking out for new stock rams, as commercial buyers usually arrive on the morning of the sale, but a red ribbon over the pen attracts the most attention of all.

We'd taken six shearling rams to the sale, Scotch being one of them, but a big homebred shearling was Aub's choice to show. While he was scrubbing the white face and legs of his entry, I wandered out to look at the female judging which was happening first. As I watched the judge, a definite carcase man, handling and selecting his front line, I realised that Aub's big gangly ram that may well sell extremely well the following day, was not going to be the judge's choice.

"We'll take Scotch out, not that one," I said.

"Course we won't, don't be daft."

"You go out and see what he's selected in the females. He wants carcase not size. Scotch will suit him far better than yours."

After considerable argument, which caused great amusement to our friends and other breeders in neighbouring pens, Aub, having looked at the judge's selection in the makeshift ring between the marquees grudgingly agreed.

"You can show him though. I'm not taking him out."

So I did. And when Aub came out to watch some considerable time later, when the majority of the rams had been sent back to the pens, we were standing at the top of the line.

"Which end is he selecting from?" Aub, not at all convinced that I could be in poll position asked a friend who'd been watching from the start.

"Your end stupid. He pulled Sue's sheep out straight away. Paul's in second place and doing everything he can to make his sheep look better than yours, but I don't think he will."

Aub wasn't the only one amazed to see us standing there. Another breeder walked past and smiling at me said "You still here then?"

I could also hear a few mutterings from some who realised Scotch was the tup I'd bought from a trailer when he'd been rejected at Malvern. The judge was taking his time over the first four and I was aware that Scotch could still go down a bit on the weak pastern when stood for too long, so allowed him to move forward a couple of steps and then back into place. The judge looked long and hard at me.

"He was smiling earlier," I said brightly, indicating the sheep, hoping it emphasised how long the judging was taking. He laughed and called for the rosettes and ours was red.

No one could believe it, least of all Aub and me. First prize shearling ram at the top commercial ram sale in the UK. I put Scotch back in the pen while the ram lambs were judged, then we returned to the ring for the Championship with the other first and second prize animals in the sections and held our breath.

Once again the judge scrutinised all the sheep, checking he hadn't missed anything. His winning ram lamb was smart. He asked me to move Scotch alongside him so he could handle both together, pondered his decision, then called for the rosettes and Champions sash which we had won.

There followed an exhilarating evening of congratulations, official photographs and celebratory drinks. Scotch changed hands the following day for a very acceptable amount of money, eventually secured by the judge himself. We started to feel we were getting there.

Chapter Twenty-Five

Directorship and Exports

In 1999 Tom Redman approached Aub about standing for directorship of the Texel Society.

Tom had been our local area director for a number of years, but had decided not to stand for re-election at the end of this term. He thought that Aub was an ideal young breeder to follow in his footsteps.

This was such a compliment. Tom was not one to give credit if not due and to consider Aub for such a post was quite an accolade. I can't remember who else was put forward but Aub joined the board of directors that Autumn and became much more heavily involved with the breed and the Society, something he really enjoyed. This did mean he had to find time to attend several board meetings during the year and be at the Society's AGM, which was starting to progress into a social weekend and was always good fun.

Our flock was increasing in quality now, with new rams being purchased and pedigree lambs of lesser quality sold for meat. Sometimes, however good both the ewe and the ram, the bloodlines didn't click. This can be seen in racehorses, where a mare mated to one stallion will breed a champion, but then produces a lesser specimen when put to another stallion.

Sometimes even replicated breeding practices can disappoint, but when all works well a champion can be born.

Sadly, that summer saw the first of our dog attacks. A neighbour, arriving home late and very much worse for wear, let his two labradors out but forgot to get them back in. Our shearling ewes, including Scotch's daughters, were in the adjacent field, and the two dogs having herded them up, attacked them. Most of the poor animals were unable to escape through the metal park railings, although we did lose four, never to be seen again.

At least ten were either dead or had to be destroyed. A further seven needed long-term veterinary treatment and never lambed, having had their tails and back ends so badly savaged. Although the neighbour, totally distraught, agreed to pay all expenses, he was surprised at his total bill. What he couldn't compensate for were the breed lines we'd lost overnight. With the majority of the Scotch daughters gone, we were relieved to have a very good ram lamb from him, 'Miserden Elan', who turned out to be a great stock tup, but he could never replace his sisters.

By now we were renting all of the farm at Sudgrove. Our commercial ram customers were increasing. As several were Agricultural colleges, we were now recording the lambs' growth rate, muscle depth and fat cover with Signet, and these colleges often utilised the figures in student lectures. The Royal Agricultural College at Cirencester had already been buying rams from us for several years when they asked if they could bring students round to see the flock and discuss pedigree ram production. We happily agreed and this arrangement is still ongoing.

Amazingly, for college visits, we seemed to fill the sheep

shed with students and most were really interested, especially a mature student from St Helena, Arthur March. He asked if he could return and look at the sheep later in the year. Arthur turned out to be deputy head of agriculture in St Helena, and after his second visit we arranged for two Miserden Texel rams to make the trip to the island to improve their meat production.

This was the start of our exports and a new era in our pedigree sheep production. The trip to St Helena was probably the most testing for any of the stock we've exported, as they travelled by boat for over two weeks, safely penned on deck although in sheltered accommodation.

Although this first export deal was arranged for us locally, and the rams taken from the farm, in 2006 we sent a further three rams to St Helena. We delivered them in person to Portland Bill and were fascinated to watch them, along with everything else, being loaded on board, having ensured that a crew member knew how to feed and care for them.

The RMS St Helena was unique, being one of only two ocean-going vessels in the world still carrying title of Royal Mail Ship. Built in 1989, specifically to supply the Island, she carried all their goods and supplies from wind turbines to vehicles and their spares; sheep, goats, and Christmas turkeys to furniture and food. Everything going there had to be carried by ship. She could also accommodate over 150 passengers as a cruise ship, taking in Cape Town and Ascension Island. The sheep seemed to cope well with the trip and each time arrived in good condition and worked well.

Several years later I contacted their Department of Agriculture to check all was well and whether they wanted more. I was assured that, while they had been delighted with the lambs produced from the Texel cross, wool was a waste product for them as they had no facility to deal with it. They had moved on to using wool-less Dorper rams.

By 2000 we were finding it non-stop hard work running the flock with Aub working full time. The large estate Aub was working on was now being run by contractors and had taken on a different aspect, so Aubrey was happy to accept redundancy when offered. Unfortunately the house was tied in with Aub's contract, but eventually this was resolved. That August Aub became a self employed farmer and contractor and we were able to rent the house.

Now I could look forward to having him as a full time shepherd the following spring.

End of year shows and sales became much more fun together and we often went as a family. Both children enjoyed the fun and atmosphere of the County shows and the sales, with the overnight stays, often sleeping in the trailer. Previously one or other of the children would accompany me to sales, if possible.

I remember a ten year old Mark going with me up the M5 and M6 to Chelford, one of the bigger Texel sales. After a fairly sleepless night in the trailer, I took him to the Auction café, where he demanded to have everything for breakfast, plus chips! Both the lady behind the counter and I queried whether he could really manage all this, but he assured us he could, so she kindly cooked up chips to go with the usual breakfast products.

He tried very hard to eat everything, but failed, then spent the rest of the day a funny shade of green without actually being sick.

While home sales were good, we still took sheep to the major

National sales and in September we had some superb shearling ewes forward at Builth NSA sale.

Looking through them at home, Aub was reluctant to take one of his best that I had pointed out, as he wanted to keep her for breeding, but I persuaded him she must go. She stood square, had tremendous back end, but her strongest feature was her white hair highlighted on her face by a big black nose and black tear ducts.

"You've got a Scotsman judging so she'll need a good head as well as a strong body. This one could stand a chance of winning in the show and make good money."

The judge had pulled our ewe forward to head the line-up in the pre-sale show, when the second placed ewe escaped from her handler, another well known Scottish breeder. The NSA sale is held over a large area and this ewe certainly covered the majority of it, with the handler's family in pursuit. We kept seeing glimpses of her in the distance, but while the chase endured our judge continued to place the sheep in front of him, ours still heading the line.

Eventually an exhausted handler, and a sheep puffing like a dragon, black nostrils extended, showing off all the sparkle of a champion arrived back in the ring. The judge indicated for her to be placed second to our ewe, where she had originally stood. Having earlier looked a lesser sheep than ours, she now looked strong competition, but after Aub had caught the judge's eye and glared at him, we were awarded first place and later Female Champion.

Chapter Twenty-Six
Foot and Mouth

2001 was not the year we anticipated. Our lambing was well underway, Aub and I both able to give our full time to the sheep, when the news broke.

People always think they'll remember where they were when something traumatic happens. I know where I was when Elvis died, but I can't remember where I was at the outbreak of Foot and Mouth. Probably just another day on the farm and we caught it on the news in the evening.

The disease was not confirmed until 20th February, when it appeared that infected sheep had travelled to Hexham market in Northumberland and Longtown, on the Scottish borders, whose name is synonymous with the outbreak. An Essex abattoir also suspected the disease in a consignment of pigs on 19th and conformation came the following day.

Foot and Mouth is a highly infectious viral disease that affects all cloven-hoofed animals including sheep, goats, cattle and pigs. The symptoms include blisters in the mouth causing increased salivation, and on the feet, causing lameness. While not actually fatal, it is so debilitating it makes stock worthless and the virus is highly infectious.

I think initially the farming community was stunned. How? Where had the disease come from. The last time it was seen in the UK was 1967 when it was fairly well contained to North West England and North Wales, although it was a major drama for farming families in those areas. But how had infection returned again?

This question was never answered. Livestock was now being imported from throughout the world, and meat coming into the UK from countries rife with the disease such as South America and Asia. Some of the pigs in one of the earliest outbreaks were found to have been fed untreated swill, which could have included imported food. Other theories ranged from animals eating waste sandwiches with imported meat fillings to government directives to cull an excess of British livestock, but no conclusive evidence was found.

Never, since wartime I imagine, had the news been watched so avidly by so many families. Had the virus spread? Was infection closing in? Whole family's livelihoods were at risk. Farming families in infected areas wouldn't leave their farms for risk of transmitting the virus. Wives lost income from outside jobs. Children missed school.

Initially we had no outbreak in Gloucestershire, but two bordering Counties, Hereford and Wiltshire, were not so fortunate. Neighbours sent pigs to an abattoir at Devizes only the day before infected animals arrived there. We closed all our gates and our footpaths, and welcomed no visitors.

We were lucky as our farm was a long way off the main roads, at the end of a 'no through road', so passing traffic was not a problem. More feed was ordered as soon as possible, and the lorry thoroughly disinfected at the gate before we let it through, but the driver was able to assure us he'd not been in an infected area at all. We couldn't get away from the strong, unpleasant smell of industrial disinfectant used to spray the vehicles each time we returned to the farm; it was nothing like the subtle smell of pine or floral household disinfectants.

Lambing was underway and our erratic timetable for meals and sleep meant we caught odd afternoon news bulletins of the outbreak and its effects on others. The general public was at first alarmed at the health risk for themselves and their families, with memories of BSE. Then they worried about food shortages, but few seemed to understand the real plight of affected farmers.

There was compensation, of course. But what compensates for the loss of all your treasured stock? Few livestock farmers are in this industry for money, otherwise they'd have pulled out long ago. Contrary to popular belief, our British livestock farmers produce a product because they have a love and empathy with their animals.

If you counted the vital hours spent on difficult lambings and calvings, often in the middle of the night, then money blurs into insignificance in this job. Monetary compensation would be a lifeline for some but probably totally inadequate to cover the losses borne.

It was interesting how our involvement with the EU took policy for treatment of the disease and disposal of animals out of British hands. In 1967 animals were killed and buried on farm in quicklime in a move to effectively and efficiently contain the disease. With European policy this was not acceptable in 2001, meaning carcases were travelled around the country for disposal by burning.

With the closure of so many local abattoirs, animal

movement to slaughter around the country far exceeded that of 1967. These movements were highlighted when the disease spread countrywide. Spring was not kind to us in any way. The weather was foul, with rain almost every day and night. Lambing continued with a wary ear on the news. From 23rd February there was a general movement ban for livestock and a suspension on hunting and point to points. By 24th February the disease had spread from Northumberland to Devon.

1st March saw a suspected case at Woolstone, only five miles from Cheltenham. Preparations for the Cheltenham festival were halted and it was postponed until April but as the disease progressed, it was abandoned. This was one of the first episodes that highlighted the financial impact to those outside farming. The racecourse, although insured, lost money. Guest houses and hotels lost bookings. Jockeys, trainers and owners lost out on Festival prize money as did pubs, clubs and taxis.

The disease was moving closer. March 11th saw the first case in the Forest of Dean, where sheep roam freely over large areas of common land. On 12th there were plans to destroy ½ million healthy sheep trapped by movement bans in winter grazing areas, where forage had all gone. There were often adjacent fields of grass, but if this meant the animals had to cross a road the government decided that it was less risk to kill them. No wonder farmers were outraged by government decisions.

March 13th saw the first outbreak of F&M in France. It was reported that there were over 1000 farms within 10km of the infected farm, which had imported sheep from the UK two weeks earlier. This news was slightly disconcerting because several British sheep had been on the stand at the Paris show when the outbreak began in the UK. The majority of the stock had been purchased by the breed society it was representing and sold to French farmers, but two sheep breeders wanted high compensation for their rams or for them to be returned to the UK at some point, so these two animals were sent to a farm nearby for safe keeping. These rams were now being moved to safety further south in France.

Back at home I had my own problems to contend with. I managed to frighten myself one morning and in doing so hit upon yet another challenge suitable for a game show.

It had rained overnight, as it did most nights. I had worried about the poor lambs outside, but they were all bright as buttons the next morning. While Aub was busy in the sheep sheds I took the quad with the trailer laden with food and hay down the bank to the bottom field, and although in AWD, the quad suddenly slid sideways and the trailer started to overtake me. It was worrying enough for me, but as I turned around to see what was happening, I saw that both sheepdogs, sitting on the back of the bike, looked absolutely horrified. Thankfully I managed to stop, regain control and continue at a slower pace down the rest of the hill to the bottom field. I could hear echoes of the MD saying, "Why were you going that fast?"

I hadn't realised I was. Still, as always, I expect he was right!

Having negotiated that bank, I cautiously drove into the first field of ewes and lambs and thought what a great game: trying to drive fast enough to keep forward motion while avoiding ewes and lambs who felt I should speed up to the trough.

I wondered whether a player would score more for running one over or for avoiding them. I reached the end of the troughs in one piece, which was quite a surprise. Equally surprising all seemed fit and healthy, present and correct and most ewes seemed to have the required two lambs with them.

Next I set off to the rams. Having managed not to get thumped the previous day I thought I'd try to get the food in first today rather than filling hayracks, especially as one hay rack seemed to have disappeared down the far side of the bank. It looked as though success was in sight until I realised that the ram's troughs hadn't drained like the ewe's ones, so had the delights of trying to tip water out of six troughs while holding a bag of food out of reach and not getting thumped. Definite game show material.

Having succeeded to a certain extent, I was well aware why our pheasants looked far better than the neighbours' as only eighty percent of the food seemed to arrive in the trough. I successfully retrieved the missing hayrack, pushing and shoving it back up the hill with the quad, though at some points going back faster than forward. I managed to secure it in such a position so hopefully wouldn't have to repeat the operation tomorrow.

Finally, the singles who rushed the gateway because they considered it bad policy to be last to be fed, then galloped all over the troughs making it almost impossible to put the food in. If we were dealing with Mules or any type of commercial sheep, the dogs would hold the sheep back while I fed, but neither dog attempted to do this with Texels. A head count revealed one missing. That was odd because I could see the whole field and wasn't aware of a sheep away from the main flock. I peered down over the bank and found Jumbi bumbling around out of sight of the trough.

"Oi, Jumbi," I shouted. She looked up, engaged brain and

galloped up the field baaing indignantly on the way because it was all my fault she missed the grub run.

Jumbi had been with us for four years, but I thought her days may be numbered this year as she'd shown signs of arthritis during the winter. She was one of triplets whose mother we suspected sat on her and paralysed her. After intensive care treatment, bottling, heat etc which kept her going for about three days a decision had to be taken as she still couldn't stand up. Aub hated having to destroy anything, so put off the fateful moment until later in the day. When he had psyched himself up sufficiently to commit the deed he strode into the stable where Jumbi was, (always a mistake to give these sickly lambs names) where she promptly staggered to her feet and baaed indignantly at him. She never stopped baaing since.

Back in the yard Aub wanted to know what had kept me so long.

By 17th March there were 293 outbreaks of the disease, mainly in Cumbria, Dumfries and Galloway and several in Devon. This was still not a crisis in the eyes of the government. However, when another 46 outbreaks were reported later that week the army was called in to help with the logistics. It would probably have been more appropriate had their manpower been utilised in the killing and removal of infected stock rather than just the logistics, though their intervention did appear to be a step forward. By 21st March the running total was 435 infected farms with probably the same number of dangerous contacts who had their livestock slaughtered.

The daily chores of lambing continued. Madonna with the big boobies lambed and I spent the next 24hrs convincing her lambs they could get tits the size of hers in their mouths. Aub had obviously relented at culling in the autumn, when her udder had not looked so huge, though I'd marked her to go. This had to be the last year I'd struggle with her. It was easier, but time-consuming, to milk her out as she milked like a dairy cow, and bottle the lambs until they grew strong and independent enough to sort out the difficulties of suckling from her themselves.

The night shift was always Aub's, and I could have ignored the phone call at 1.30 in the morning, but it wouldn't have helped much.

"I've got a problem," he said.

"Oh yeah?"

"Yes … I'll be back in a few minutes. Put the kettle on."

Great. I was being woken at 1.30 in the morning simply to make the coffee.

When he returned, however, it appeared that he was worrying about a ewe who had put out a water bag earlier but hadn't opened up enough to lamb.

Although due fairly imminently, she probably wouldn't have started yet, but having barged her way forcefully into a small space at the feeder only to be squashed, she had forced our hand. Texels were such pigs at meal times, they could have twenty foot each and still fight over one select part of the feeder.

"I can only get one finger in so I hoped you might manage better to begin with, with your smaller hands," said Aub.

I grunted.

"We needn't rush, good idea to leave her a bit longer."

Why wake me this early then, I thought. My brain wasn't operating properly yet.

On investigation, the ewe didn't show any signs of opening up at all and by 2.30am, I suggested it looked like a vet job and a caesarean. It was the middle of the night, costly and the chances of any live lambs might be remote but there wasn't really any alternative.

Twenty minutes later Tom appeared. He was the latest edition to the veterinary partnership, but had been there a couple of years now so we accepted that he had done the odd caesarean before.

After satisfying himself that the ewe did need a caesarean, Tom started laying out his necessary equipment on the strategically placed sheet of plywood we had prepared next to the makeshift operating table: four bales covered with a plastic sheet. Luckily the weather wasn't as freezing cold as it usually was for night time operations and we'd placed the table at the back of the sheep shed out of the wind.

"Whose helping me with the lambs?" Tom asked, having prepared the ewe for surgery.

"Me, I guess," I mumbled.

"Well, when we've got her on the table and tied her legs securely you'd better put this gown on," he indicated to a green gown sealed in a plastic bag. Why was it the older vets did the job so quickly, just handing me the lambs to towel off, their only concern being to do a neater stitching up job than the others, while the younger vets took ages to follow all required guidelines. Just experience I supposed.

As I pulled on the gown I realised here was yet another man who thought I was 6ft 4in with legs up to my armpits. I was more likely to break my neck in this outfit than add any form of hygienic assistance, but there you go.

After tripping up twice I asked Aub to tie a piece of baler twine round my middle and hitch the gown up, with vague memories of Farmer Fred's oversized coat with the baler twine belt. Eventually I did manage to towel life into the three lambs in turn, with Tom taking time out to blow air into their lungs as they were a bit early, but all looked successful. While the ewe was being stitched I took all three lambs through to the warm box, a home-made plywood structure with warm air blown into it from a fan heater, which I'd switched on earlier, leaving them to warm up thoroughly before I fed them colostrum and returned them to their mother.

Once stitched, given antibiotics and looking comfortable she was taken to a large pen with room to come to terms with her family. She started licking them. After checking all was well with the other sheep and double checking the ewe and her family were happy, it was almost five o'clock when we drove home to bed. At least, Aub went to bed while I elected to sleep on the settee. I had slept earlier and one of us would need to check the shed again by seven o'clock.

The day progressed without its usual clarity after our disturbed night. Aub rose about ten and we turned out another lot of ewes with lambs to clear some space for those who seemed to have gone into overdrive.

Heather was moving to a new flat, but discovered her bed was too big to go in her car, so that afternoon we found time to collect it for her. With F&M outbreaks in Wiltshire it took a lot to persuade Aub to come, although I did point out that Hev and I couldn't do it on our own. Taking the bed to pieces was not the easiest of tasks, Aub muttering about why she couldn't stay in one place long enough to wear a bed out, which caused raised eyebrows from both of us, not quite sure if he had thought through the implications.

"Dad's ever so ratty isn't he?" said Hev.

"We're both quite tired," I explained. "Had a caesarean early this morning."

"Well I should have an early night tonight. You both look as though you could do with it," she said. There speaks the understanding of a non-interested farmer's daughter during lambing.

At 4pm when we did a final check of the outside sheep, a super ram lamb in the top field had managed to rip out his ear tag, tearing the ear from end to end. Once he and his mother were back in the shed, I rang the vets again to clarify that we couldn't take the lamb in because of F&M movement restrictions but were grateful for their instructions on how to repair the ear ourselves.

While I drove into town to pick up local anaesthetic and needles Aub caught up on five minutes sleep. Supper was solved by a visit to the chip shop and it was nearly 9 o'clock before we started to repair the torn ear. Aub administered local anaesthetic and when the ear had been numbed started his row of neat stitches on the top layer of the ear to be followed by a row on the underside as instructed by the vet. Ears have a strip of cartilage in the centre of them and this does not have great healing potential, so it was essential that both the top and bottom layers of skin were connected without sewing through the cartilage. Aub decided as I was incapable of even minor repairs to his clothing, I would be totally incapable of stitching an ear and he was probably right.

"I'd better put a couple of stitches in the bottom," Aub said. "What are you doing?" he asked in amazement as I slid off the feeder and closed my eyes.

"I don't think I can hold it while you do that," I said pathetically. "I don't feel too good."

"Well move over then so I can hold him while I do it."

Suddenly feeling faint I lay flat out, face down in the straw, (which luckily for me had recently been freshly bedded,) and breathed heavily trying to avoid the nausea swirling over me.

"Are you going to sleep down there?" an irate voice enquired.

"No, I feel ill," I moaned.

"You are pathetic," I was told with disgust.

"A little sympathy wouldn't come amiss." A period of silence followed.

Eventually, through gritted teeth he replied, "I can't hold this lamb, stitch up the ear and be sympathetic. Sit up and hold him while I finish."

I staggered to a sitting position, feeling very green around the gills and held the compliant little chap while Aub concluded his handiwork. I went home to bed while Aub stayed awake long enough to do the final midnight check when thank goodness, no one appeared to want to produce.

The following day there were 59 more outbreaks of F&M.

Chapter Twenty-Seven

Spring turns to Summer

The early morning was serenaded by the dawn chorus. As the day broke, the beauty of the Cotswolds began to unravel. Streams of mist floated across the fields in front of the sheep shed. It was a moment to value and remember.

One of Madonna with the big boobies' lambs had already learnt how to suck her, thank goodness, and overnight the other had caught on. Her saving grace was she always had plenty of milk.

No one was looking imminently like lambing that morning, so once we had fed, hayed and sorted lambs in pens I started the drugs run. On the list was an old girl with mastitis we had picked up yesterday, and a gimmer who wasn't looking brilliant. She'd had a boost drench and was eating her hay, so now she was just given a top up of antibiotic in case slight infection was causing her problem.

I offered her lambs a bottle as her milk was not that prolific at the moment. I gave a final long acting jab to the ewe in the bike shed who had slight hardening of her udder and turned her and her lambs into a bigger pen to recuperate, then treated the lamb with the stitched ear and the ewe who had had the caesarean. Only five more ewes to lamb so the work load was lessening.

About a week later the last ewe lambed at 6 o'clock in the morning. When I arrived at the shed, she'd obviously been on for a while and had a problem, but had no desire to let me catch and help her. With eyes the size of dinner plates and the turn of foot of a racehorse I realised I'd never catch her on my own, let alone lamb her if she was as frantic as she implied, so drove home to drag Aub out of our nice warm bed for assistance. It was certainly a joint effort to hold her down while Aub sorted out the difficulty, but what a relief to have finished lambing.

Another Texel breeder, Christine, had rung to borrow our spare warm milk feeding bucket, so at lunch time we drove down to deliver this, although we elected to meet in a lay-by just off the A48 as she was close to outbreaks near the Forest. We explained the intricacies of the bucket, discussed the ongoing F&M problem and decided it was time to organise a 'clean' party away from any farms where our local Texel breeders could all enjoy a social, as by now we were aware that spring was going to merge into summer and we would have no shows to go to.

Next morning we found a lamb on the top fields with a broken hind leg, dangling from the hock. Eventually, Aub caught up the ewe and other lamb in the trailer while I carefully carried the injured party on my lap on the quad. It was broken above the hock, but with movement restrictions still in force would mean a vet's visit to set it which would cost more than the lamb was worth, so once again we were down to basic first aid.

While Aub held the lamb and its leg still, I wrapped the leg in cotton wool and using two splints covered these with a sticky bandage, finished off with parcel tape. The lamb was not too impressed, but obviously it was still hurting.

I gave him painkillers and penned the ewe and her lambs in an individual pen. The following day he was struggling to suck and not looking his best, but the leg seemed to be securely bandaged without being too tight so Aub decided to let them into the main pen with three other ewes and lambs and the lambs would have access to the creep. This was obviously the right decision because the injured lamb soon started to improve. He was obviously sucking regularly and going in for creep. He had to be restricted and kept bandaged for three weeks but looked as though he'd cope.

The weather improved as we moved into April. A beautiful sunny day was enough to make me feel good to be alive and that all was well with the world. It was silly really. The government joined in with the April Fools jokes by still trying to reassure us the F&M wasn't out of control, then by the afternoon it was raining again.

Cheltenham had been abandoned, but Aintree was determined to run the National although they must have had even more rain than us. Here it was a beautiful, sunny day. The second lot of lambs age wise were wormed and coxi drenched before putting the 55 ewes and their lambs on the Ruin, the driest and most sheltered field we had, if you could class that as a category at the moment. We finished for lunch just in time to watch the lead up to the National. A total mud bath of a race. Of 40 starters only four finished and two of those were remounted after falling. Miraculously no horses were killed, but I bet there were a few dodgy legs to be felt the following day.

The lamb with the broken leg was coping well. I found him cavorting about in the hay rack next morning, something that requires agility. He was taking some weight on the leg now, so ER eat your heart out. Our combined first aid looked to be working. The ram lamb with a torn ear looked great too, although I wasn't completely convinced the ear was ever going to be his best point.

I spoke to a fellow Texel breeder that night who had lost all his stock to F&M. I realised I'd seen his name on the website but his address hadn't meant anything to me as we'd only met up at shows and sales. He rang during the evening and just needed someone to talk to. The pain he was suffering from his loss was so immense I realised all I could do to help was listen and offer comfort. The frustration he was feeling from lack of advice and information from MAFF was turning to anger, which was probably a good sign. He hadn't left the farm since his animals were destroyed over a week ago, though they hadn't been removed for another four days. His wife was working but he just felt he couldn't leave the place without taking the infection with him. We did, however, persuade him to meet up with us for lunch, bringing his wife with him. She was so relieved he'd agreed to come out. It really brought home the awfulness of the situation.

It was soon raining again and blowing hard. Looking out of the kitchen window in the half light of evening, the feed bag Aub had tied over the footpath sign was bobbing up and down in the wind. Seen against the big tree behind, it looked every bit like a body hanging from a gibbet! Spooky!

Unbelievable news today. MAFF, in all its wisdom, was bringing the carcases of dead beasts from the Berkeley/Dursley area up to Aston Down, about four miles away, to either bury or burn on an old airfield recently sold to the Princess Royal. I doubted she'd had a say in this. It was frighteningly close to a large pedigree Hereford herd when as yet we were a clean area, but the government worked in mysterious ways!

I weaned four of my bottled lambs the next day, moving them from their warm milk machine to a larger pen where they would continue on the pellets, but exchange their warm milk for water. Surprisingly they didn't complain too much, though the two younger ones left behind were furious. The following day the four bottlies, having now realised that the warm milk had ceased, were objecting quite forcibly. They'd been joined by another lamb whose mother had mastitis on one side and was kicking him off, a typical result of this cold wet weather. He wasn't too happy about the arrangement but it was the best option and he soon settled down.

We had a strange summer with no shows and no visitors to the farm. What we did have was days of birdsong, the sky larks trilling away on every sunny day. Lapwings appeared where we'd lost all thought of seeing them and other wildlife relished the security of no walkers or dogs. Interesting that the loss of our wildlife and birds are so often blamed on farmers.

The end of September saw the last confirmed outbreak of Foot and Mouth, but it was January 2002 before the country was declared clear of the disease. There had been 2030 confirmed cases in the UK with a total of over 6 million animals slaughtered and a cost to farming of over £900m. Compensation to farmers whose animals were slaughtered to prevent the virus spreading or for welfare reasons topped £1.34 bn. Tourism and the rural economy was estimated at having losses of £5bn. The following spring the hills of Northern England echoed with silence. The sheep had gone.

Ram sales in 2001 were difficult. There were still restrictions on movements although Defra, who had now taken over from MAFF, did allow for breeding stock to be moved, as long as they were licenced and recorded. Typical government, the printed paperwork asked what sex the rams were, male or female!!

Farm to farm sales were popular, but prices were down. It was a year when there had been no markets to assess fair prices and lamb producers had had to deal with abattoirs who had treated them badly, so no one could buy expensive rams. Farmers could be offered as little as £20 for a prime lamb, but the general public didn't see any drop in prices.

Our local abattoir was as bad as the rest, offering similar prices for top quality lambs, so we decided we'd sell them ourselves. Armed with details of our prices and where the lambs were reared, I traipsed round local pubs and restaurants and spoke with local caterers and shops.

As we mainly sold pedigree breeding stock, the numbers for meat were limited, but the quality was first class. We needed to earn a reasonable price, which was about four times what the abattoir was offering and luckily the majority of the outlets I sourced were happy to take our lamb, some still being regular customers today.

Chapter Twenty-Eight

Rams back from France

The year following Foot and Mouth brought more excitement.

There were two rams lodged in France. The owner of one wanted his ram to be returned to England or to be paid a substantial price for it, so Aubrey and Steve, the Chief Executive of the Texel Society, travelled over to bring the pair home. We were aware the French were troubled about the English sheep being near Paris and had moved the rams further south. What Aub and Steve didn't realise until they were in France was the distance involved.

Licences to move livestock were still difficult to obtain, and only granted for a limited period of time, so speed was of the essence. They found the rams on a smallholding about five hours drive from Paris. Arriving at nightfall and aware the weather forecast was not good, they loaded the sheep and left at first light to catch the ferry home. However, at Calais they were horrified to discover the captain would not take the sheep on board as the sea was too rough.

After deep discussions, pleading and begging, the captain was obviously not changing his mind, so they searched for alternatives.

Finding themselves a hotel for the night, they fed and

watered the sheep in the trailer, where there was plenty of room for them to lie down, and parked it with the ramp tight to a wall, so no one could steal them. Aub's suggestion at this time of stress was to drop the ramp by the quay, let the sheep loose and catch the ferry home without them, but they refrained.

The following morning they managed to contact the captain of a container ship on the Norfolk line leaving Zeebrugge. When told of their predicament of timescale the captain agreed to take them, with the warning of a rough trip. I don't imagine the vehicle touched the ground with the speed they drove from Calais arriving just in time to catch the ferry at Zeebrugge.

Settled comfortably in the lorry drivers' lounge and restaurant, they agreed the weather report had been greatly exaggerated, not realising the boat was merely sailing down the coast to Calais before turning and crossing the channel. The forecast was totally accurate.

Aub is not the best sailor at any time, but I gathered things were not going too well when I phoned to check he'd remembered to pick up my French cheese.

"Not the best time to ask him, Sue," said Steve. "He's a funny shade of green at the moment."

The ferry pitched and rolled across the channel, eventually attempting to enter the port of Dover, but the wind was catching the superstructure of the boat making it impossible to line up with the harbour entrance. After several attempts the captain announced he would try one more time but if not successful they would have to lie up along the coast until the wind dropped. Aub must have felt like death at that point, but the captain did manage to straighten the bow and took them into the relative calm of the harbour.

They waited to disembark, relieved their dramas were all over, until they discovered another just beginning. A number of surrounding vehicles were being moved out of the way and blinding blue lights appeared in front of them. It was then Aub and Steve realised the police were after them. Escorts with flashing lights, one in front, another behind, took them to a customs building where they were locked in. Eventually someone came to speak with them.

It materialised that their import paperwork for the rams, which had been faxed across from Zeebrugge ahead of their arrival, had an incorrect stamp. Either it was square when it should have been round or vice versa.

By now, both men had justifiably lost their sense of humour. After the long, exhausting and sickening few days all they wanted to do was deliver the damned rams to the isolation farm and get home to bed. Finally the paperwork was sorted out, but on their drive home officials from Defra phoned to say they would have to stay overnight at the isolation farm, in the car, as they were too late to wash out and disinfect until the morning. Aubrey made a quick phone call and arranged for the wash-out to stay open until they arrived. They dumped the sheep, drove to wash out, took possession of the certificate and came home.

As they both commented later, after all that trouble, no one heard or saw anything of this expensive ram once his owner had him back.

Chapter Twenty-Nine
Blue Texels

Our venture into Blue Texels came quite by accident. We purchased a lovely Texel ram lamb, Rascarrel Jack the Lad, from Scottish breeder, Tommy McTaggart.

He was a stunning sheep that we ran with a fair number of ewes that autumn, although as always, we were careful not to over-indulge a ram lamb.

We looked forward to seeing his progeny in the spring and they did not disappoint. However, one did surprise. A great ram lamb, with classic head, stretch and muscle, came out with black and white spots. He became quite a talking point. Aub rang Tommy to ask how his ram was bred! I think the conversation included a mention that although Aub knew Tommy bred British Blue cows, he wasn't sure how this had warped into the sheep breeding!

The Blue Texel was a fairly recent breed to be introduced to the UK. As this lamb acquired a blue roan colouring as he grew up, we decided he was one. He was incredibly striking and we called him 'Miserden Klinker'. Partly from his colouring and also his outstanding conformation.

We were taking Texels to all the major shows, so I entered 'Klinker' in the Any Other Breed class at Three Counties, the

Royal Show and the Royal Welsh. He probably attracted more attention to the new Blue Texel breed than it had seen before, people constantly asking what he was, and admiring his stature. I think our pen at that year's Royal show was one of the most visited. He was 1st prize ram lamb and Reserve Champion in all three shows, which was quite an achievement for a lamb.

The Texels were also doing well in the show ring, our homebred ram lamb 'Miserden Kracker' taking centre stage. He and a couple of exceptional ewe lambs formed our show team and won at a number of shows.

The following summer, much to our delight, 'Miserden Kracker' was white Texel Breed Champion at Three Counties Show and 'Miserden Klinker' was breed Champion in AOB. We have the cards and rosettes framed and hung in the hall, as I never thought we'd win two championships at the same show in the same year again. I was later proved wrong as with both Blues and Texels we've done this a couple more times at different shows since.

Kracker and Klinker were great friends, travelling together to the shows, both coming 2nd in huge classes at the Royal Welsh and winning again at Moreton Show at the end of the year.

After the considerable success with Klinker we decided we'd better look into the breeding of Blue Texels. We soon realised he was really too strong a sheep for that breed, having the body of a white Texel even though his colouring was Blue. However, he had duel registration and left us some very good white Texel lambs and once we purchased some Blue ewes, some very good Blues.

The Blue Texel has come to us from The Netherlands, where

two white Texel sheep with the recessive colour gene, mated together, produced the Blue lambs. If we think back, sheep have had coloured fleeces for thousands of years, but when wool was discovered as a clothing material, white sheep were selectively bred. This made the wool easier to dye, leaving only the primitive breeds with their natural coloured fleeces. However, the Dutch were very taken with the carcass quality of their Blue Texel lambs and soon discovered when they bred these blues together, they retained both quality and colour.

Smaller and lighter of bone than the Texel, the Blue Texels have narrow heads with good length of neck, making them ideal easy lambing sheep. With the colour being recessive the majority of lambs from white ewes will be white, appealing to commercial farmers.

There were not many Blue Texels in the UK at this time, so we went on a small shopping spree with some friends, Andrew and Sylvia, to a retiring breeder's dispersal sale held on his farm in Wales. There were plenty of prospective buyers there, Blue Texels just starting to become very popular. Looking round the pens Aubrey decided there were three ewes he really liked, one being the mother of the other two yearling ewes.

"Blues are going to be yours, so you can bid for them," he said. So I did, glancing back at him as the price rose higher than I was expecting.

"Leave that one," Aub said, as the older ewe went to higher bids than we felt she should. "Bid for her daughter."

I stood in by Clive, the auctioneer, as this lovely yearling ewe came into the ring. Far smaller than our Texels, but with great conformation.

The bidding progressed at speed, but we wanted her, and I bought her. She was followed into the ring by her twin sister.

Obviously distressed at being separated, she took three big bounces across the sale ring, then leapt up onto the rostrum and into my arms.

"I take it you're buying this one as well Sue?" said Clive, and of course we did.

We had also been very taken by the stock ram in the pens and when he entered the ring I bid for him, but again his price was going up at speed. Eventually, when he reached 1500 gns I appeared to just be bidding against one other.

"Let him go," Aub urged. "You've only got two ewes. He's too expensive."

I agreed. Congratulating his eventual purchaser after the sale, I realised our rival bidder thought he was going to buy the ram for far less than he ended up paying due to our involvement.

Andrew and Sylvia had bought three older ewes and decided they needed a ram, so they asked Aub to select a ram lamb we could share. We took a fresh look at some we had seen in a shed on the farm, which had not been entered in the sale.

Aub picked out the ram the breeder had planned to show the following year. However, discussion and notes changed the breeder's mind and Marteg Merlin came home with us.

Merlin and our two fantastic ewes were a tremendous investment as foundation stock and their near perfection passed through all their progeny. The ewes consistently bred us top class sons and daughters, grandchildren and great grandchildren; some retained in the flock, some sold to other breeders. The original ewes lived until they were ten and eleven.

As enthusiastic Blue Texel owners, Sylvia and I went to the Blue Texel Sheep Society's AGM the following January, when, for various reasons, the Society's officers were all standing down. It suddenly looked as though there was not going to be a Blue Texel Sheep Society anymore and we'd just invested in the breed.

"Do you fancy being Secretary, Sylvia?" I whispered.

"Well, I suppose I could."

"I don't mind being Treasurer," said another new member. "I've done it before for another Society." So that was decided.

"If I've got a good Secretary and Treasurer, the Chairman's job can't be too daunting," I said, and this was how we found ourselves as officers for the Blue Texel Sheep Society for the next six years!

The previous secretary had sent out interesting newsletters every other month, which sounded great, except that we soon discovered that most of the paperwork relating to member's details and those of the sheep were housed in a shoe box. Sorting it took many hours over the next few years.

Joining forces with Libby Henson and Grassroots, we updated the original constitution and rules, and set up a system that allowed the organisation to receive sheep registrations electronically. When the time came to hand over to the next in line, I was really pleased to feel how far we had come in securing the breed in the British flock books, and spreading knowledge of Blue Texels to commercial farmers.

Chapter Thirty

30th Anniversary Celebrations in Crieff

With Aubrey a director of the Texel Sheep Society, one of his annual commitments was attending the Society AGM. Never one to miss a party, I usually accompanied him. Initially it was a meeting only, held in Scotland, Northern Ireland, Wales and England in rotation, until it was suggested a full social weekend would be appreciated by members. This evolved and was thoroughly enjoyed.

Along with others, Aub was involved in sourcing the right venue for the Society's 30th Anniversary Celebrations, which they decided to hold at the Crieff Hydro in Scotland. While there were mutterings from southern members about the location, finding accommodation for over 250 people with built in entertainments and activities was a tough order and we all knew the Scots were more than capable of hosting a good party.

By now we were lucky enough to have Mark T, who lived locally and worked part time for several farmers, working for us one day a week. He would also look after the sheep and dogs when we ventured away to shows, sales and jollies.

On arrival in Scotland we were surprised to find the Welsh members already installed and discovered they'd arrived a day early, due to someone's error on dates! However, to fill in time they had decorated the main arrival area with welcoming banners, which unfortunately had suffered a little in overnight bad weather.

Aub helped to organise a photographic display in the reception area of the top priced rams from the last ten years sales, the layout strictly supervised by the Chairman's wife. I joined two of the girls from the Texel office for a drink, as it was a while since we had caught up. Gradually the photographic display attracted so much help and advice that Aub abandoned the project to those who thought they could do better and joined us in the bar.

Friday evening's entertainment began with the fire alarm. Having taken longer than usual soaking in the bath there really wasn't time for this before the reception and it was howling a gale outside.

"Should we see what's happening?" Aub said.

I muttered that I'd only got makeup on one eye so of course I couldn't. After a while there seemed to be a lot of activity in the corridor outside, so we wandered along to the next bedroom, where the girls from the office appeared in their underwear and dressing gowns.

"I'm not going outside in this." Jill was quite adamant, and did look rather skimpily clad for public exposure. At that point a porter extracted about thirty people from a Scottish member's room opposite, where the cloud of smoke following them gave a clue as to what had set off the alarm. We decided it was far too cold to stand outside so returned to our rooms to perfect the evening's dressing before meeting the crowd of freezing, irate members who'd been banished outside for twenty minutes during the fire drill.

The Chairman hosted the Friday evening reception, which was followed by an excellent meal, a vaguely amusing comedian and yet more drinking and socialising. Saturday's entertainments were varied and well supported. A number of us flocked to the Famous Grouse Experience which was well worth a visit. Others played a 'short' round of golf, which took over two hours to complete the six holes in the 'Pitch and Putt' area, one being lost in the rough on a number of occasions.

The girls from the office found themselves on the Quad bike experience, with Jill so worried that Aub agreed to go and hold her hand. At this point in his career Aub was Society Treasurer, so quite frequently dealt with accountant Jill. However, major steerage problems soon saw the end of her biking experience, deciding a drink and cigarette would be far more relaxing. Meanwhile, her friend Jean was proving to have a natural flair for quad racing. She narrowly avoided being reprimanded for excess speed and reckless driving, as were the men who returned to base having been threatened with expulsion if they didn't behave.

I foolishly chose horse riding and although my mount was safe and polite, his saddle left a lot to be desired in comfort. Staggering back to the hotel, looking forward to a long hot bath, I was pressed-ganged into a minibus and driven off to a previously arranged fashion show, hardly dressed for the occasion. Several members who had committed to go had backed out so just seven of us were forced into a tiny dress shop. Not a great turnout for the fashion show, especially when the hosts had laid on wine and nibbles.

Nothing really appealed to me, though I tried enthusiastically to find something to buy with Aub's money. Sally looked great in one outfit, Kate found a nice top and I liked some silky black trousers. Not having my glasses with me (you don't always on a horse), I struggled to make out the price tag. Thinking £8.50 rather too cheap I asked Kate to check. We decided they really weren't worth £85, so, after purchasing a book about the shop owners' pet brown bear, we rushed back to prepare for the AGM and the evening's entertainment: an elite in-lamb sale.

The AGM passed quietly, followed by the somewhat depleted number of gimmers to be sold, as some proved not to be in lamb. A misprint in the catalogue made interesting reading, stating that Tommy and Fiona had previously sold females for 62,000 and 70,000gns. If Tommy found the cheque, he promised to take Fiona out for a meal.

The black-tie dinner and presentations were the highlight of the weekend, where we were joined by other members not staying at the hotel. Unfortunately, the only place large enough to host so many was the hotel's gym, which was noticeably lacking in heating. This did take the edge off things for the more scantily-clad ladies. A good meal led us onto the raffle and the auction held for charity then drinking and dancing went on into the small hours with Bernadette leading the Welsh contingent with great enthusiasm well into the night.

Chapter Thirty-One

Exports

Blue Texels stole the show the following spring when we were visited by a group of Norwegian farmers. Both Texels and Blues were running together and our guests were taking photographs of the flock when a Blue lamb strode forward to introduce himself. The Blues have always been bold and nosy, but this had everyone laughing.

The previous year a number of these Norwegians had used 'Miserden' semen on their ewes. Norway did not have a protocol to take live animals, but semen was allowed in and our good ram, 'Miserden Orient Express', was just the type to improve carcase. He had all the best breed characteristics without an excessively big head or being too strong of bone. Some ewes had already lambed and the farmers, delighted with their progeny, were excited to see both the ram in the flesh and more of his lambs on the farm.

The summer rolled on with successes at shows and great interest in our sheep. The National Sheep Association's Sheep Event is held at Malvern every other year and attracts a large number of foreign visitors. We had very short notice of a visit from some Swiss farmers, wishing to see Texel sheep on farms prior to the event and only the night before their visit, realised they had come to buy, not just look!

As usual the weather was little help. Early that morning we rushed round in the rain, making sure the right sheep were accessible for viewing and handling and after a very wet scrutiny seven ewes and two rams were purchased. The Swiss entourage was led by Heinz, who had already bought a number of British Texels, and along with several friends he was looking for more ewes and a couple of rams to join their flocks. Though Heinz spoke excellent English, we were delighted to meet Kathrin, the Swiss interpreter, who kept everyone on the ball.

Just as we completed our tour of the farm and were heading back for refreshments, we were joined by a French couple, also going to Malvern; they selected a ram lamb to go to the French National Texel Breeding Stud. This was followed by an order from Germany, joining the Swiss shipment.

The Swiss and German export ran smoothly. Not so the French. Having had a number of discussions via email and phone with the purchaser to organise a travel log, he eventually gave me the dates he and a friend would come to the farm. They planned to stay at a B&B overnight then go on to Wales to buy sheepdog puppies, leaving their trailer with us.

I was horrified when I saw the trailer. It was similar to the one we towed with our quad. The tarpaulin across the top came down over the air vents, but our Frenchman assured me it was fine. While the pair were in Wales, I had several conversations with Defra in Carlisle about the travel log, their main concern being the Frenchman had no number for his transporter's license. We agreed I'd send this to them when he returned from Wales, the day before the export.

"Transport license? We do not have anything like that. In France we do not need a transport license," he said in his limited English. Reporting this back to Carlisle they assured us both that

France was part of the EU and, yes, he did need a transporter's license. However, on this occasion there was a loophole: as he was only transporting one animal he could take the ram lamb as a pet. This was confirmed and settled before our Frenchman opened the boot of his car to show us the five sheep dog puppies he was also taking with him, with absolutely no paperwork. They all looked well grown and healthy, but I was horrified.

"We need a vet's signature," he said. "To say they are all healthy and vaccinated. "You have a vet we can see?"

"No I don't," I said. "Our vets won't sign anything for you. They won't have any idea if they've had vaccinations; didn't the people in Wales arrange all this?"

This was a typical 'under the carpet' deal we could do little about. With all the relevant paperwork from our side, we loaded the ram lamb and issued the Frenchman with a water container, bucket and some hay. He left for Dover. We imagined he got everything through customs and on to the ferry with the poor little puppies smuggled in the car boot. The ram arrived safely; we hoped the puppies did too.

Exports could be straightforward or a total nightmare. We sold some Blue Texels to Northern Ireland in 2014, when Janet and Andy came over to view and collect the stock. All went smoothly. However, the following year, when they arranged haulage to transport more Blue Texel ewes, things were not so simple. This particular haulier transported livestock all over Europe so I had not anticipated problems. The paperwork for export to Northern Ireland is not as daunting as for other parts of the world, but it does exist. A legality of which some Irish seemed unaware. A travel log needed to be prepared and sent to Defra.

The travel log states hours of travelling, rest periods and normal details like vehicle registration numbers, licences etc. The Irish job was proving a little testing. Seamus, the company owner, was poor at answering emails and when I telephoned he assured me he would ring back in five minutes. Obviously there is a different time scale in Northern Ireland as I am still waiting for that call. His next communication was to suggest that the driver of a lorry he had coming down the M5 could meet us at Worcester Market at midnight. I declined, pointing out we would not have access to Worcester market in the middle of the night, nor any intention of being there at that time.

I progressed with my side of the travel arrangements, alerting Carlisle of the date we anticipated the sheep leaving. They could forward the reams of paperwork for our vets to complete, who would then health inspect the sheep within 24hrs prior to them leaving. I told our vets not to panic, as although we should have the licenses through, I had not yet had dates confirmed for the sheep to be collected. These proved an interesting few days. Janet in Ireland had had no contact from Seamus and was hoping the sheep would be collected on Friday 17th September, according to the forms. I eventually contacted the elusive Irishman who assured me he had a lorry going to Belgium the following week which, on its return, would pick up the sheep from the farm.

It was arranged for the sheep to be collected around four pm on the 25th. Tamsin, our vet, inspected the sheep at the farm that morning, then we sat at the kitchen table to complete and double check the paperwork.

"Will the lorry registration be the same?" she asked, ticking off all relevant points.

This hadn't occurred to me. We both decided it was unlikely so I rang Seamus yet again.

"Oh b' Jesus, does it matter?" he shouted down the phone. "No of course it isn't." After a lot of paper rustling he came back "Look, use this one," and gave me another registration.

Tamsin looked at me, raised an eyebrow and we both laughed. Who was to know what registration lorry was to arrive? Did it matter? At that point it didn't. Any problem at the ferry would be his.

4pm came and amazingly so did the lorry. And what a lorry. Fortunately we had brought the sheep to the home farmyard as the lane to our farm was extremely narrow. However, it was so enormous he couldn't even get into Lypiatt farmyard, where we have had some fair-sized trucks.

The driver was a great Irish guy. He explained he had taken sheep out to Belgium and now, after securing the five sheep in the front of the bottom deck, kitted out with automatic drinkers and hay, he was off to Macclesfield to fill up the rest of the lorry with beer to take back to Ireland. Some return load! After he'd had a cup of tea and taken the necessary rest time, we backed our trailer up to the lorry's ramp and the ewes trotted into their new accommodation and settled down quite happily. Amazingly, all went smoothly from there and they did arrive safely with our Irish friends.

The last load of that season went to Estonia, but travel arrangements seemed to take forever as others were going on the same trip. Earlier in the year seven incredibly tall Estonians had visited and selected rams they wished to buy, including two Blue Texels. We explained about the recessive colour gene and the unlikelihood of producing many Blue lambs, but they were taken with the carcase quality, lighter bone and narrower heads. Tall these gentlemen may have seemed when we chatted at the farm, but when we returned to the house, the sitting room seemed overpowered by them. Not one was under 6ft 6ins. They found it quite amusing and assured us that they were no taller than most Estonians.

At the end of October the haulier informed me that he would be picking the sheep up at 4am.

"Great!" I said to Aub, since exporting sheep was not always as good as it sounds. "Do we go to bed and get up early or simply sleep in the chair until the lorry arrives?"

This was solved by a later phone call saying he would be with us by 1am, so again we had the sheep, four massive rams, in the trailer at Lypiatt ready for collection.

It is never particularly easy reversing the trailer back to meet a lorry ramp in the dark, but our driver assured Aub his positioning was okay. I did point out a small gap between the two sets of gates but no one seemed too concerned. With interior lights in the lorry reflecting off the clean metalwork, it sparkled and was not particularly inviting for the rams. Instead of them walking across from one ramp to the other as compliantly as the ewes bound for Ireland, the rams refused to leave the security of their trailer, so Aubrey got in to push them out. That was when things started to go wrong.

The rams were still not keen and one of the larger ones spied the small gap between the gates, the gap I'd pointed out and was now trying to block. At the same time another chose to escape on the opposite side. At 1'oclock in the morning in the pitch dark we appeared to have lost our consignment to Estonia.

"I've got him," I shouted as I wrapped my arms around my escapee and stuffed his head into the straw stacked in the barn. I was able to hold him there while Aub and the driver recaptured the other three.

"Not sure whose got who here," said Aub, as both the ram and I appeared to be going deeper into the bale. However, we soon persuaded him to join his friends and gave a sigh of relief when the lorry departed.

Chapter Thirty-Two
Huttwil Show, Switzerland

As a direct result of meeting with the Swiss Texel breeders in July, Aubrey was invited to judge their major pre-sale show in Huttwil near Zurich, in November. We were incredibly lucky with the weather, as while we bathed in warm sunshine and tremendous Swiss hospitality, it rained non-stop at home.

We were welcomed at Zurich airport on the Friday, driven to our hotel, then went on later to several farms to look round their sheep. The Swiss all had full time jobs; their sheep were a hobby kept on small acreages near their houses, with neat and tidy farm yards.

I made a note to self to tidy the yard when we got home.

Later we joined all the breeders we'd met at our farm for a wonderful traditional Swiss raclette supper. It was great fun. Most spoke some English and all had a terrific sense of humour. The food was superb; the first time I've had warm cheese on potatoes and peaches, which I can definitely recommend.

Saturday's show was held in part of a huge woollen mill, with the sheep penned in a big wooden barn. It was a crisp, chilly morning, the surrounding fields glittered with silver frost and the backdrop of snow-capped mountains was most impressive. This was the only annual auction of Texel sheep in Switzerland, with just thirty sheep offered for sale. It was fascinating.

All imported sheep were first put before the Swiss inspectors who judged them for conformation. They simply looked at the sheep and only handled their wool. A grading mark was then awarded for conformation, pasterns and wool, with a maximum score of four awarded to lambs, five to shearlings and six to older sheep for each component. This meant a shearling with a score of 'five five five' was judged as top class.

The handlers brought their sheep out individually for judging on the concrete yard, but many of the sheep fought against this, not having been handled before, so it was difficult to see if they stood correctly. When it was Aub's turn to judge, he handled the sheep for muscling and checked their mouths. He then asked for a pen to be erected from spare hurdles, where he could see the animals loose, so he could judge their pasterns and locomotion properly. This was something new to the Swiss. They were suitably impressed and decided they may well use loose inspection in the future.

Once Aubrey placed his winners in each class, the entries were judged again by two German judges, clad in long black smocks, looking like large ravens. They eventually placed the sheep in quite a different order to Aub. They were looking for good bodied sheep, as was he, but with narrow heads, similar to Lleyns. Keen on strong pasterns for good locomotion, they were not worried about mouths, hocks or feet that turned out. All in all an interesting day giving us an insight into where both the Swiss and Germans placed their importance when selecting sheep.

Lunch followed, with time to look round the vast woollen mill and gift shop, then we wandered outside to see alpacas, camels and for the first time Swiss Valais Blacknose sheep, who looked so at home in the alpine setting. Garments made from all these animal's fibres were exhibited in the woollen mill.

The afternoon sale was unlike anything we'd ever been to before. Each individual sheep to be sold was run up a ramp to the sale ring, which was on a trailer. This proved a good place to view the animal, bidding taking some considerable time, but with only thirty forward this may have been intentional. Top price of 1740 Swiss francs, (£1155) was paid for an imported British Texel, which was most satisfying.

Our weekend only got better with Heinz and Franz, another Texel breeder, taking us on a round trip of Switzerland the following day. We headed for Interlaken where Heinz took us to visit Kathrin and her husband, who lived on a mountain above one of the lakes. They had striking Gotland sheep grazing on the slopes in front of the house, with Simmental cattle grazing up into the mountains behind them.

The sheep wore decorative bells with thick leather straps and Heinz presented one to Aubrey. We then drove on to the cabin Heinz owned, his summer grazing on the Alpine slopes extending down to the lakes. Even in November it was magical and easy to visualise happy summer holidays his family must have there. The weather was amazing and the hospitality of our Swiss hosts second to none. Only too soon it was back to Zurich and the flight home.

Chapter Thirty-Three

Lock Down at Lanark

The National sales are the pinnacle of the Texel breeder's year. Most of us strive to breed at least one or two quality breeder's ram lambs, the major flocks usually ten times that number. These will come from breeders all over the United Kingdom, to be sold at several sales, but the best will be aimed for the Scottish National at Lanark. This is the most prestigious sale on the calendar and the holder of the top price record for a six month old ram lamb, 220,000 gns (£231,000), the price of a small house.

While this seems a huge amount to pay for a sheep, we are talking the top end of pedigree breeding and the potential for the new owner to make over a million in lamb and semen sales. Maybe not achieving top price, many breeders would expect their Lanark lambs to make serious four and five figure prices throughout the day.

Six years after the 2001 Foot and Mouth epidemic, it appeared the livestock industry was to receive another almighty blow. The Texels entered for the Scottish National had been inspected by Aubrey and the Society vet and were installed in the market ready for the pre-sale show. Moments later Steve received a call to say there was a suspected outbreak of Foot and Mouth from the Pirbright research station. This meant an immediate standstill of all livestock movement.

Luckily the official vet for Serad (Scotland's equivalent of Defra), who deals with all animal health matters north of the border was an extremely sensible man. As all the animals had been inspected, although simply for teeth and testicles, he felt any obvious signs of illness would have been picked up. However, he did instruct the vet in charge to go through the sheep again looking for any signs of Foot and Mouth. This was completed, with the alarming result of two gimmers from one breeder showing signs of sores on their gums. Ministry vets were immediately dispatched to the breeder's farm to check all his sheep at home.

While this was ongoing the directors were informed that no animals or people could leave the market. By now the roundabout approaching the market was patrolled by armed police, doors were locked and the market gateway blocked. The police were even making arrangements for sleeping bags to be supplied for the night. Aub and the other directors passed on information as they received it, but by late morning there was, understandably, considerable unrest. The implications of a disease breakdown, in both financial and breeding terms could be devastating. Should anything positive be found, all these top class pedigree breeding sheep would have to be slaughtered!

After discussion, the board members decided the best plan was to open the bar, putting a substantial sum on a tab. This took very little time to be consumed, but tensions eased slightly. Talks continued with the Serad veterinary office, who liaised with Defra and Daera as a fair number of animals had come from England and Northern Ireland. Fortunately nothing at the breeder's farm was found to have any sign of Foot and Mouth. Ministry vets then examined the two suspect gimmers and again the decision was made. This was not the dreaded disease.

Although the sheep in question had been given the all-clear by the afternoon, there was no guarantee the sale would get the go ahead the following day. In normal circumstances the morning inspection is followed by a show in the afternoon, with females sold in the early evening and rams the next day. On this exceptionable occasion the society directors, along with the auctioneers, made the decision to sell all the sheep that evening. Buyers needed these rams for their imminent breeding season.

The show was held, followed by the sale of all the sheep, which ran on into the early hours of the following morning. Essentially it turned into a breeder's sale, the majority of buyers also being consigners, although this would not be unusual in a normal year. A few local buyers were able to get there at short notice, but others not aiming to arrive until the following day, sadly lost out. Although less sheep than usual changed hands, with others going back home, the auctioneers reported it as a remarkable sale under the circumstances.

Foot and Mouth was confirmed, thankfully only within a contained area surrounding the Pirbright Research facility, but with that and Blue Tongue it was not the best year for farmers!

Aub arrived home mentally and physically exhausted. He had already inspected the Northern Irish sale. He was due to inspect the English sale at Worcester and the Welsh at Llandovery in the next couple of days.

Chapter Thirty-Four
Groundhog Day

Lambing was soon upon us again, with the same old routine, rather like Groundhog Day. No small hairy creature emerged to predict the time of spring, though there were plenty of others who did. Each day seemed to follow the same pattern, with a few variations gained from earlier mishaps.

I was glad mud was good for the complexion as I was plastered in it most of the time. Overnight it had rained non-stop and it was still pouring as we checked and fed the sheep in the morning. Aub was not his usual bright, cheery self. He seems more affected by the weather than anyone else I've ever met. He frowned and growled and bit my head off.

Things did not improve by the quad running out of fuel halfway round the fields. Rain ran down the back of our necks, the bike was strongly addressed, but still refused to fire up when turned onto reserve. After considerable kicking and pulling, the battery appeared to be dead. Aub eventually got it going, but was not happy.

Added to that, I couldn't find the two lambs belonging to an old ewe on the top banks. I eventually discovered that, sensible as she was, she had stationed them under the old holly tree out of the worst of the weather while she waited for breakfast, looking pretty depressed with life.

"Can't imagine why!" was the sarcastic response from my spouse when I told him.

"You are foul this morning."

"What's there to be happy about?" he said. "I'm soaked and cold, so are my sheep. The lambs are up to their necks in mud and now it's snowing. I've never seen water running out of these banks like this and we're up on the top. Perish the poor sods in the vale. And you expect me to smile?"

"Yes," I shouted back. "I'm fed up with having a miserable husband, and I want to get this ewe and lambs back into the shed before we have coffee!"

The ewe was a dear old girl who, over the years, had given us two sons who won at the Royal Show as lambs. She was still doing a wonderful job of rearing two lambs, but I think these weather conditions were just about the last straw. Catching her was no problem, but one of her lambs seemed to have little understanding of how far it could push Aub on a day like this. Finally we unloaded the ewe and captive lamb from the trailer and I walked the three of them back to the buildings, where she gathered considerable speed once she realised her destination was a nice shed in the dry.

Earlier, while Aub fed the singles in the top field, our trusty sheepdog Nell and I turned some ewes with twins into the two acre. According to the weather forecast they were unlikely to stay out long, but it was always better to get them out for a short while if possible, whatever the weather. Although they had made this transition from shed to field and back for the past three days, today, like Aub, they wanted to be somewhere else.

I ended up with a definite deterioration in my language with sheep going everywhere except the right place. Poor Nell was totally frustrated as the ewes ignored her completely. At one point I had two of the thirty with their lambs grazing in the two acre with the remainder elsewhere, in and around the yard. Eventually all the ewes made it to the correct field, leaving me with three lambs. Eagle (a former pet lamb who should never have been named and kept) had, as usual, abandoned both her children and another ewe had left one behind.

Even though I got this one lamb out to the field, it was unable to find it's mother and insisted on running back to the shed. In the end I left all three inside. The ewes were only going out for a couple of hours so no one was going to starve in that time.

While Aubrey brought more big bales of hay and straw out of the barn, I took a load of small straw bales down to the bottom field in the trailer to provide little windbreaks for the lambs. It was actually more sheltered down there than I'd dared to hope, though not my idea of a pleasant place to spend an afternoon, let alone a night. Driving back on the quad the snow hit me head-on with bullets of ice making it impossible to see where I was going. Nell bowed her head, glad to hide behind me, saving her a little from the icy impact.

Cold and saturated, I bedded up, so the wet lambs still coming in at nights would have somewhere dry to sit, although the sheep shed was rapidly filling up with wet snow. Later on it was good to see them snuggled down in fresh straw and made all my efforts worthwhile.

The doubles came back in before the weather got too bad although the lambs looked fairly cold and wet, but the weather had turned to blizzard conditions before I could bring in the singles. I had an awful job separating the ewes from the sheltered wall and tree stumps they had selected for their lambs' protection.

The following morning we gave a sigh of relief to discover all the lambs outside had survived the night's blizzard. I hoped my straw windbreak made their night more bearable. I don't know why we worry so much. The lambs are nearly two weeks old and Texels are renowned for their hardiness. But it had been a cold bleak night.

We transferred most of the remaining ewes and lambs from their individual pens into a bay of the main shed during the morning, to ease the workload a little. All the same, Aub was getting increasingly fed up with moving sheep around; his idea is to get them out as soon as possible. These were unlikely to be turned out yet, unless there was an improvement in the weather.

But, as always, the weather did brighten up. While no great rise in temperature it was dry and eventually sunny. This, lambs can stand. It's the constant wet on their backs they hate. Similar to the shepherd!

The big bale of hay we'd just opened in the barn smelt of all the summer warmth and fragrances imaginable. As I buried my nose in the bale I was once again lying in a warm hay field, the burr of the tractor and rake sounding in my ears, the sun hot on my back. Sensations like these make farming worthwhile.

Chapter Thirty-Five
Transylvania

By now Aubrey was representing the Society at a number of agricultural exhibitions all over Europe and gaining great interest in the Texel breed. From his contacts at these exhibitions and our involvement with British Livestock we received several requests from farmers wishing to visit and look at our stock.

We first met Romanian farmer, Christian, and his father, when they came to see our sheep and ordered several rams and breeding ewes. While Christian bought white Texels, his father was very taken with the Blues and we agreed for one ram and two females to join the consignment.

Arrangements were made for the usual medical precautions of blood tests and inspections, and transport agreed when an Englishman moving to Bulgaria contacted us. We were able to add several ewes and two rams to the Romanian consignment and travel costs worked out favourably for both parties. Those going on to Bulgaria would be collected from Christian's farm.

The following spring Aubrey was going to Agraria, the agricultural exhibition in Cluj.

"Why don't you come as well?" he asked.

"If Mark's happy to look after things, yes. Why not."

So I decided to join him. We shared the British Livestock stand with other exporters. Cluj Napoca is the busy capital of

Transylvania in Romania. I'm not sure what I expected to find, but we didn't meet Dracula.

We stayed at the striking, new, family-run Hotel Paradis, which looked strangely modern surrounded by blocks of concrete flats, reminiscent of communist buildings. The oldest son told us the hotel was previously very small, but they had 'boofed it down' and rebuilt it five stories high. He was so proud. It was a magnificent building with comfortable rooms and an underground spa.

They were a family of football fans and hosted visiting international teams when they played at the huge Cluj Napoca football stadium, including Manchester United. We stayed at the hotel three or four times. One year a major tournament was being televised and the son had wired the television units for football only. He was amazed when we asked if he could get us a channel without football, but after about twenty minutes he managed to isolate the television in our room and give us an alternative.

Agraria was quite a small exhibition when we first visited. Held at the beginning of April, when we were still enduring rain and cold in England, the balmy twenty-three degrees of Cluj was a welcome change. However, the buildings, mainly fibreglass, had no air conditioning initially and it could be sweltering inside, although we and other exhibitors soon organised ways of letting in air through windows, doors and even a hole in one wall!

There was great camaraderie at these events. In the long warm evenings we all met up for drinks at pavement bars, chatting and watching the locals before finding a nearby restaurant for supper.

An interpreter accompanied us throughout the exhibition, as without one trade would have been impossible. The only trouble with some of them was that by day three they considered themselves sufficiently knowledgeable on the livestock, be it cattle or sheep, to answer the questions without consulting us. This meant we needed to be explicit about passing the interested parties to the right representatives on the stand, which generally worked out in the end.

Our young female interpreter on the first year felt repressed by the lack of communism and complained the majority of Romanians were lost without their guidance. This was contrary to our interpretation of their freedom from communist rule, but some had obviously found security in that situation. Possibly she was a little extreme in her thoughts as in future years we found the student interpreters had come to terms with the situation, although lack of employment, even with qualifications, did seem dire.

Days at the exhibition were both fun and hard work. Everyone in Romania produces some sort of hooch: from the rough clear liquid found on the farms at 99% proof, to the more refined with added fruit juice, offered by Romanians on neighbouring stands. It would have been rude not to accept, but occasionally I did think 9.30 am a little early to participate. We often indulged later in the afternoon. Just small shot glasses, not pints!

Because we had a number of people helping on the stand, Aub and I were able to take time to wander round the rest of the exhibition, looking at both machinery and especially the livestock. This helped us to see the type and breed of their indigenous sheep and we found the Tsurcana (Turcana) and

Tsigai (Tigaie) to be the most commonly used. The Tsurcana was best described as a cross between our Swaledale and a goat. They were tremendous milking sheep, and cheesemaking was the major reason for farming sheep, but the growing interest in Texels was clear. To produce milk the sheep must lamb, but if a proportion of those lambs have better conformation they are more valuable animals.

Romanian's themselves only eat lamb at Easter time. A family will cook a whole, small lamb at six to eight weeks old. The rest of their lambs will be exported. Farmers generally wanted the lambs weaned in about eight weeks. They would then milk the ewes and make cheese, their staple and main source of income. I have no idea what type of cheese we sampled in Romania, but often, on the farm, it did not look terribly appetising. A soft, young cheese, sometimes near white, but more often a fawny grey colour. Some we were offered had little flavour, though other samples with more added salt were good.

All the farmers were most hospitable and every farm we visited, however small, laid out a wonderful picnic of cheese, olives and hooch, which Aub kept quietly pouring away but still finding his glass refilled.

Over the years we visited the country we did our utmost to educate the farmers on their marketing. Most were so wrapped up with cheese production they found it difficult to comprehend that their lambs could possibly provide them with a far greater income.

A farmer would contact a haulier to take all his lambs, from the very small to any we might consider fit, the majority being exported to Italy. No price was agreed at this point. When the lambs had been sold the farmer would receive payment, which did not appear to amount to much.

In our search for younger, more forward-thinking farmers we were pleased to visit Christian on his farm several kilometres outside Cluj. In Romania none of the owners live on their farms, having houses in the towns and cities. Building was not permitted on agricultural land. The difference between the city of Cluj and the surrounding countryside was almost a century apart. We drove from the hectic five lanes of manic traffic in Cluj city centre through to dirt roads where most of the transport was horse-drawn. We saw an elderly couple moving sheaves of hay on a horse-drawn wagon with the mare's foal trotting happily alongside. Lining the sides of these roads, where we might expect to see telegraph poles, were tall poles with large metal bowls set high on the tops for storks to nest in, and we saw several huge birds sitting.

Shepherds tend the flocks on foot and they just kept on walking, something else we tried hard to explain. Ewes needed time to stop to mother up their lambs once they had given birth, but still we saw these constantly moving flocks with thirty or forty misplaced lambs following on behind, snatching a suck from the odd ewe they were able to catch before being kicked off. It was one of the saddest sights on the farms, and seemed so difficult to educate the shepherds.

Christian and his father ran the farm with many staff. Christian, in his early thirties, knew all the tricks in the book to claim EU grants. On our first visit, the farm appeared to be just a huge expanse of grassland which backed on towards the Carpathian Mountains. His shepherds and their families were based in a small encampment surrounded by expensive machinery scattered around, obviously left out in all weathers.

The shepherds themselves lived in an array of shepherd's huts and similar shacks, with one of the tractors constantly running to give them their energy supply and run the television.

"Where are the sheep?" I asked Christian.

"They are up on the hills, but I'll have them brought down," and he rang one of the shepherds to bring a flock down for us. This surprised us. Everything seemed so basic, yet all the shepherds had at least one phone, often two as signal could vary from different suppliers. After some time sheep emerged from the higher altitude grazing. Each flock appeared to be of 400 – 500 ewes with lambs and were escorted by several large Pyrenean type guard dogs who formed part of the flock along with a selection of donkeys. The shepherds had some smaller dogs, a sort of cross between a terrier and a poodle who were their working dogs and moved the sheep.

The ewes, mainly Tsurcanas had a mix of Texel cross and pure bred lambs on them, but Christian soon caught up some of the Texel cross lambs, produced by our rams he'd bought the previous year and the difference in quality was obvious.

"These lambs have to be worth more money," he said, but agreed that unless he could persuade other farmers in his area to improve their marketing it would be difficult to get them to use better rams. Christian was quite determined to continue with the Texels and seek a different marketing strategy, in which he could hopefully involve other farmers.

He sent that shepherd away with the first flock and rang another one who brought down a similar flock from a different direction. When I queried the dogs and donkeys in with the flock he told us that both were good at attacking wolves and even bears, occasionally to be seen on the hills. The donkeys were also used to carry the shepherd's camping gear when they moved longer distances for seasonal grazing. A third shepherd brought the rams up for us to see. They looked in good condition and appeared to have acclimatised well.

By the time of our next visit to Christian's farm some three years later, he had built a huge sheep shed to house his sheep at lambing, with conveyer belts moving forage to simplify feeding. Next to this stood a massive building full of top of the range machinery. Both his lamb production and large arable acreage were obviously benefitting from all available EU grants.

I nearly didn't make the event the second time as bad calculations meant we had six ewes due to lamb around the time of the exhibition. I elected to stay at home with help from Mark T. Aub had booked his flight and accommodation earlier in the year. The week before he was leaving I stood in the sheep shed studying the ewes and thought 'these damn things aren't rushing to lamb.'

Two days before Aub was due to leave I checked the weather for Cluj to discover it was sunshine at 27 degrees C. It was cold and wet here.

After a quick chat to Mark and the offer of a bonus for anything he had to lamb while we were away, I managed to book the last seat on the plane. This was quite a feat, as the Wizz Air flight to Cluj Napoca only flies once a week.

Fortunately Aub had booked a double room. I would have been so fed up if he had rung with a weather report when I was stuck at home in the cold and rain. I was even more delighted when Mark sent me a text the day before we returned saying 'Two ewes lambed. Had vet out 4am for one!' Rather him than me. Never mind the bonus; I was getting too old for the night shift.

By now the exhibition had extended to three times the original area, with numerous pens of livestock on display. We saw lambs bred from our Texel rams, which attracted a lot of attention and left us hopeful we were getting the message across. Each year we had farmers who showed great interest and invited us to look at their farms. Without that insight we couldn't send them the type of rams they wanted or offer any advice.

One farmer took us quite a distance out of the city, only to park in a layby on a busy duel carriageway. Then, like Christian several years before, he rang his shepherd who brought his flock down the hill to the side of the road. It was amazing. The sheep were so used to wandering where they were taken and stayed in a quiet mob on the wide verge while we looked through them, never venturing onto the road. Then again dismissed, this flock was replaced by another coming down from a different stretch of the hill. Finally we drove a hundred yards further along to see the flock on grassland the opposite side of this hectic road.

It proved difficult to explain that without fences it would be impossible to segregate these flocks for breeding. A ram in one flock, once his ewes were quiet would move away on the lookout for others in season. Should these be on the other side of the duel carriageway, this could cause him little concern, although might shorten his lifespan.

We asked whether the farmer had any fenced areas where he could mate the sheep, so he could cross some ewes and keep others pure Tsurcana for replacements. He assured us he had had such an area, about ten acres, but once he had fenced it, he had sold it!

It was at Cluj we met up with one of the most forward thinking of our Romanian customers who had travelled up from southern Romania to see us. Mercia was a businessman, his main enterprise a large haulage company. With his wife he also ran a small farm, producing strawberries and asparagus, for which he had established markets with the restaurants in Bucharest, near his home of Constanta. Now, he intended to provide these restaurants with quality lamb, aiming to set up a small pedigree Texel flock to produce rams to mate with the local sheep breeds. After dealing with so many Romanian farmers who had little idea of marketing, Mercia was a breath of fresh air. Not only would he sell his own lambs to the restaurants, he would buy in Texel cross lambs from farmers who bought his rams. Mercia came over to England to select his sheep, taking ten ewes and two unrelated rams. His breeding and marketing enterprise has gone from strength to strength.

Chapter Thirty-Six

Saudi Arabia

Eurotier in Hannover, Germany, is a huge agricultural event held in November every other year.

We visited, and found that livestock and machinery covered around thirty massive halls in an exhibition complex. Animals were shown and paraded in the hall where we had our stand; other halls housed machinery, milking equipment and every other agricultural item you could imagine. While Aub was again representing the Texel Society, this time I went in our own right, representing Miserden Texels.

Eurotier was definitely the most International of all the exhibitions we attended; a top class showcase for all countries. Although we had interpreters on the stand, every group of Russians and Chinese brought their own interpreters with them and they were there to buy. While there was no protocol for us to export to these countries at that time, we were aware they would find a way to import them.

Over our four day visit we had considerable interest in the Texels, not least from a couple of young men from Latvia. Sadly, what they wanted they could not afford, so their requirements changed every day, but at least they proved entertaining. At first they wanted six thousand Texel rams then decided they could be lambs not mature rams, before dropping to our suggested reality of buying a small pedigree flock of 10-15 females and 2 rams. With others on the stand we placed bets on the likelihood of them placing an order! In the end their confusion was obvious and we suggested they went home and thought about what they wanted and contacted us later.

More constructive was the interest from the United Arab Emirates, which materialised into an order for 20 females and 5 rams the following February. One of the Sheiks from the UAE was desperate to improve the quality of his country's livestock. It was an unusual setup. The farming members of his community would only accept new breeding stock he had bred, not any bought in, which meant setting up breeding flocks of his own. His Irish farm manager Mick, joined forces with Mike Adams from British Livestock soon after the exhibition and they travelled all over the UK with a shopping list of different breeds of sheep, as they were not sure which would work best in UAE.

Mick had the choice of over thirty of our Texel females to draw from and quickly selected twenty. One of the advantages of the export trade is they rarely require what we in the UK prize as the best Texels. They want a sound and correct sheep with good conformation, but narrower in the head and often smaller than our British buyers favour. In no way were the animals selected for export inferior to those sold at home, simply different specifications for different jobs. Again, with the rams, we would only select those with correct conformation but lighter in bone with narrower heads. All these characteristics suited the purchaser as the sheep would be run totally commercially with little or no assistance available at lambing time.

Our sheep were to be part of a consignment of nearly 200, and as space in transit would be at a premium, they were rapidly sheared, then housed in deep straw, as December was not the time of year we would usually do this to them. Mick and Mike had long discussions on transportation, the obvious answer being to fly the sheep out to UAE, but the quotes coming in were astronomic. Sheep were being purchased from both the UK and different parts of Europe, so eventually ours, plus others sourced in the UK were driven to Schiphol airport in Holland where the Sheik had his aircraft used to transport his race horses pick them all up.

Amazingly all went without a hitch. Having had our concerns about the sheep coping with the temperature, Mick assured us they would be living in air-conditioned buildings. I knew this was often how they stabled their horses and believed him. Mike was the lucky one who travelled out with them to ensure their welfare. On his return we gathered they were living in large bamboo sheds with palm leaves as roofs, the Arab equivalent. Never believe the blarney of an Irishman! However, we were happy to learn they adjusted to the lifestyle, even if the long hours of daylight made the breeding programme less successful than previously hoped.

Chapter Thirty-Seven

Sheep Fairs

September was hectic. Aub judged at two Sheep Fairs, we attended two major shows, winning two Breed Championships at Royal Berkshire, and sold sheep at three breed sales. Ram buyers visited the farm to purchase new stock in between everything else, and meat lambs made their way to the Carpenters Arms, our village pub, and private freezers.

Sheep Fairs have been held all over the UK for many years, wool being the foundation of the wealth of the nation from the Norman Conquest of 1066, and a number of these still exist. Our local Barton Sheep Fair, originally a sheep and cheese fair, was held in Gloucester from the 13th Century right up to the closure of Gloucester cattle market at the end of the 20th Century, although the sale name has been resurrected at Cirencester market. By the end of the twelfth century, England's most important industry was the production of wool. Contests were held, ribbons awarded, and farmers and their families would exhibit and sell their wide array of sheep at these fairs.

This September we had the privilege of visiting two of the country's most famous sheep fairs. Completely out of the blue at the end of August we received a letter thanking Aubrey for agreeing to judge Findon Sheep Fair, on the South Downs. This took us by surprise because neither of us could remember a letter asking him to judge, nor his agreement to do so, but it was too close to the event to let them down by saying this, and any way, it sounded like fun.

Findon Sheep Fair has been held at Nepcote Green, on the downs just south of Worthing, since 1261. Sadly, now it is simply a sheep show, the traditional auction having long ceased, but still a major event in the area. While Nepcote was more like suburbia than our understanding of a village, that took away nothing of the village-like atmosphere of the weekend. Everyone joined in with the Sheep Fair in the best way they could. We, and another couple we knew who were also judging, were given the most superb Bed and Breakfast in a private house, hosted by locals undertaking their first attempt at B & B, which they did with great success.

I had received a couple of emails about our accommodation, but was surprised to have a last minute one warning us that "Nepcote is a dark village!" Did this signify witchcraft or something similar, or that they had no street lights? The latter turned out to be the case, which didn't cause us any problems, as we certainly are not used to street lights. The Fair is held on a huge village green, and manned by stewards from every walk of life, all wearing bright yellow high visibility vests with cartoon sheep on. There was everything there from plant and produce stands to an old fashioned fair ground and coconut shies. Wool was shown in all aspects and varieties and the sheep came from breeds we had never seen before.

Aub judged the Continental and Foreign breeds, his classes including some well-known Continentals, including Texels and Charolais, and some lesser known animals. Icelandics featured in a number of classes, making it quite difficult to judge these long haired almost goat like animals against the meat breeds. Another breed was Ouessants. These we had never met before. They are tiny sheep from an island of the same name, off the coast of Brittany.

About the size of a Spaniel, they produce top quality wool which is made into garments worn by the islanders. Although they come in varying colours, from cream to many shades of chestnut and red, black is the predominant colour and the fibre is used to make top class fabrics worn by the older women on the island. Again, quite testing to judge against commercial meat producing breeds, but they were very correct sheep, so every breed went home with at least one rosette, and all seemed happy at the end of the day.

Two weeks later we headed for the beautiful town of Masham, set in the hills of England's picturesque Yorkshire Dales in lower Wensleydale. Boasting one of the largest and finest market squares in England, Masham was famous for its sheep sales where in the past as many as 70,000 sheep were sold annually. Driven from the surrounding moors, they were packed together for sale in the centre of the little market town. This fair, which also goes back to the Middle Ages, has now become a spectacular show, with over 100 classes and more than 500 sheep competing, raising considerable sums for local charities. The village square was crowded with wooden sheep pens full of different sheep breeds, many bearing the names of regions throughout Britain. Although some considerable distance from home, we immediately met up with other farmers we knew.

Aubrey was judging both the Texel class and Any Other Continental, both of which were divided into the health statuses of Maedi Visna accredited sheep, usually shown by breeders, and non MV accredited, shown by local farmers, one of which had an outstanding ram which Aub eventually placed as his breed champion. The farmer was delighted because he said that judges usually went for the MV breeders sheep. Although this sheep had obviously been bought from a pedigree breeder originally, Aub was impressed by the condition and the quality of the animal.

Later that afternoon a feature of the event was the Bishop Blaize procession, where school children dressed up as soldiers, kings, queens and clergy, with one lucky boy dressed as the Bishop riding a grey pony. The Bishop was patron saint of woolcombers which once abounded in Masham and this was to mark the link with Bishop Blaize and Masham's past.

More entertainment followed with sheep racing and a display of sheepdogs working ducks. Another fun weekend which showed the versatility of sheep breeders.

Chapter Thirty-Eight
Castlewellan

The summer months make farming such a wonderful job and through showing and judging at different events we have made many friends. We appreciate we are fortunate to have Mark T, who is prepared to look after the stock while we are away, otherwise we would find it difficult to leave the farm so often.

Showing our sheep to local farmers and shepherds, who later in the year buy our rams, is an essential and enjoyable part of our year. Nowadays our first show is usually The Royal Three Counties at Malvern, held in the middle of June. It is a great place to meet up with many of our friends and breeders of all types of sheep and cattle and becomes a big social occasion. While good show results are a bonus, friendship and camaraderie at these events are more important.

We set up camp on the Wednesday, prior to judging on the Friday, selecting the best spot for our caravan and running a string on electric fence posts from our caravan to secure room for friends, so we can barbeque and party together. We are now also sufficiently organised to tie on pen sheets and bed up the pens so we can unload our sheep the following day and settle them in with no delay. One of the best parts of any show is walking through the sheep pens last thing at night, ensuring the stock are happy and catching up with others doing the same.

We exhibited both Texel and the smaller Blue Texels at the Three Counties show, with all the Texels and Blues being placed. This culminated in our Blue shearling ewe, 'Miserden Amber', winning her very large class.

Besides competing ourselves, both Aub and I are lucky to judge at several shows each year. I was delighted to be invited to fly to Northern Ireland early in July to judge the Blue Texel classes at Castlewellan Show. A beautiful area, with the distant Morn Mountains making a dramatic backdrop, the show was held in idyllic parkland and involved many sheep, cattle and horse classes as well as a multitude of handicrafts, agriculture and horticulture.

The show weekend also hosted a thriving folk festival, and over a cup of tea in our hotel coffee house, we found ourselves at the launch of a book on Irish music. This involved readings about folk singers and the performance of several traditional Irish songs. A unique tea-stop.

Having only travelled to Northern Ireland before with a group of English Texel breeders, we were then based in a large hotel with organised trips. This time, seeing the Irish in their 'natural habitat', they seemed even more Irish than the English portray them!

As I listened to the folk music I looked around at the collection of people. They couldn't have come from anywhere else, especially one lean, hungry-looking man of indefinite age. Wearing a battered black leather jacket, with straggly shoulder-length hair showing under his trilby, I felt I almost recognised him. Then realised he was simply a familiar reflection from Irish comedies.

Looking around the room, I smiled to see the wallpaper on one wall repeated on part of the ceiling. Rather incongruous to have a black and white pattern of horses and carriages running above us, but perhaps not surprising.

Ireland is a land apart from others. Distance is similar to Cornish miles. When approaching a destination, the signpost often tells you there are two further miles to travel than the last sign pointing in same direction. And time is definitely not of the essence.

Our small hotel was just 50 yards from the show entrance, so we arrived on site in plenty of time for a ten o'clock start. However, as half the entries had not yet reached the showground there was time for another coffee and a tour around the craft tents, before anyone seemed inclined to begin proceedings. Without sufficient rings to accommodate all the classes I was relieved I'd mentioned to the show secretary that we would need to leave soon after 2.30pm to catch our flight home from Belfast at 4.20pm. At least this meant I was allocated a ring for the first lot of classes.

Eventually my steward starting calling for entries to come to the ring. There only appeared to be one in the senior ram class, but he needed inspecting and judging as if there were a ring full. He looked a nice ram and eventually became my Reserve Champion. A two-year-old, correct in his mouth and on his legs. I was just about to award him first prize when a very red-faced gentleman wrestled another senior ram into the ring. Unfortunately for the exhausted owner, this didn't change the placings and after looking well at the second arrival I still chose the first to stand above the latecomer. The other classes had more entries, the females being larger classes than the males. Sadly, my Champion, a senior ewe, did not make the headlines in the

Interbreed, but some of the other breeds had some excellent sheep forward.

A taxi took us both ways between the showground and Belfast City airport. The flags and banners in some of the towns we passed through illustrated just how divided Northern Ireland still remained as a country. Back at home the lambs had grown on well. It's always good to look at our own stock after judging other peoples and even better when we decide we are pleased with the majority of our own.

As summer progressed, hay and haylage had to be made for winter feed. Haymaking could be idyllic, although our rather elderly machinery could always be temperamental. While the contractor turned the main fields into big bale hay and haylage, as a family we played with the home paddock, making small bales. On hot sunny days the baler travelled in an aura of dust, its mechanical arms looking like some demented cartoon creature frantically stuffing hay into its metal body, determined to appease its hunger. The constant chug sounded similar to an old steam engine, pistons rocketing up and down. It was probably from the same era.

The sky was an endless blue. "Enough blue to make a pig a waistcoat and it won't rain," my grandfather always said. There was enough blue there to make a pig a complete wardrobe. The weather forecast was dry until the end of the week.

The sledge trailed behind the baler, ideally leaving a neat double quadrant of bales for Aub on the JCB to pick up with the grab, but often one was rejected or sometimes the baler forgot to knot the string, producing a double sized gift. If alert the baler driver saw this and jumped down to cut the strings, shake the grass and bale again on his next sweep.

The huge trees that offer welcome shade to livestock when grazing here waved their full foliage in the gentle breeze. By midday the temperature had risen. The tractor had air conditioning, but a disconnected pipe was making work hot and dusty on the JCB, the only reprieve from the heat was to have the door open.

Lifting the uniform bales was easy, the grab obligingly doing the work, depositing them on the trailer. Collecting up the stray bales and misshapen debris brought a different aspect to the job. Luckily the baler seemed to have got the hang of the job as the afternoon wore on, with just a few little offerings left lonely around the extremities of the field. The machinery may not be brilliant, but at least now it was ours.

Later in the year ram buyers had already begun arriving to select their shearlings. We had interest from Cyprus to send out a small flock of females with a couple of rams. They went later in the year when the temperature there was cooler. Visitors also arrived from Holland and Lithuania, the Dutch being very interested in the ewes.

While Aubrey had now resigned his directorship of the Texel Society after sixteen years, he still inspects at all the National Texel sales throughout the UK during August and I see very little of him during that month. September is a time for major sales and two more local shows. Our Blue Texels again excelled, winning Breed Championships at both the Royal Berkshire and Moreton-in-the-Marsh, where 'Miserden Amber' also went on to win Continental Champion and Reserve Supreme Interbreed and one of our ewe lambs became part of the winning Interbreed pairs championship.

Moreton show is always a wonderful end to the summer season. It is said to be the biggest one-day agricultural show in the country, although other shows claim this accolade too.

Friends who breed cattle, pigs and different kinds of sheep all congregate there, along with our fellow Texel and Blue Texel competitors and it is a challenge to be the best. Sometimes our best have already been sold, but often we have a star, especially in the Blues.

One year 'Miserden What Now', a really smart gimmer, not only won the Blue Championship, but went the whole way winning the Continental and Supreme Interbreed Championship. Once showing has finished the party begins, then there is still time to wander round and watch the show jumping and cattle parades, before tea and scones in the NFU tent.

With most of our commercial ram sales happening at home it was good to go to the major Builth ram sales where one of our Blue Texel ram lambs, 'Miserden Blitzen', won both the Male Championship and Supreme Championship at the Society show and sale, and sold very well to another pedigree flock.

Chapter Thirty-Nine

The Gangster

Our scheduled visit to Cluj the following year was booked before I realised Heather's baby was due while we were away.

"Well, what are you going to do, Mum?" was her question, when I said I'd cancel my trip. "However experienced you are with sheep, you're not going to deliver it, so just go. Kev will be with me and you'll be much more help to me after I've had the baby."

Realising what she said made sense I did as I was told, only to spend several hours on the phone comforting a sobbing daughter who had not had the best of births, culminating in an emergency caesarean. A modicum of privacy to converse could be found within the assortment of new air conditioning pipes, housed in a corner cupboard near our stand. While Heather was still agreeing there was nothing practical I could do, she simply needed to talk to me. We managed this at least two or three times a day.

Aside from our poor daughter's angst, this was probably one of our most exciting trips. We encountered a landowner-come-farmer, who Aub entitled The Gangster, although initially the man did nothing to justify this title.

It was only later we realised he had a bulletproof car and the utmost security on his property. Having come on to the stand every day of the exhibition to discuss his requirements, he persuaded us to visit his farm and others on the UK Livestock stand decided to accompany us.

Our interpreter was Doru, with whom we had become great friends. He was determined that after University his next challenge was to become the Mayor of Cluj Napoca, and he has probably succeeded. His girlfriend, Rosa, joined him on the stand each afternoon when she finished work and we invited them both along on this trip. Doru would have come anyway as our interpreter, but Rosa also spoke excellent English and was happy to join us. Her presence turned out to be useful as she had her car and it would have been a squash for everyone to travel in The Gangster's huge Hummer, so Doru went with the main party and I joined Rosa.

We followed the Hummer, stopping each time it came to a halt. Outside a small shop The Gangster wound down the window just far enough to whistle to a boy standing outside and hand him some money. That was when Rosa and I realised the thickness of the glass window. We'd already discussed the fact the vehicle was built like a tank. The boy returned to the car with two sliced loaves, which were quickly and neatly taken in through the re-opened gap. We followed the Hummer for several kilometres, chatting away quite happily, not really thinking about the possibilities of our partners being shot at, travelling in such an ominous vehicle.

The farm was just off a major road complex, similar in layout to a mini spaghetti junction, though not as busy. We turned off up a rough track and approached a heavily fenced area. Doru, obviously issued with a key, slowly got out of the Hummer, quickly unlocked the gates, waved both vehicles through, then re-locked the gates after us and jumped back into the Hummer just as two enormous long-haired German Shepherd guard dogs approached. Thank goodness they were more attracted to the sliced bread being thrown at them by The Gangster. Rosa and I were amazed by the dogs. They were huge.

We drove away from them, on to a further securely fenced area, where Doru risked life and limb once more, having to unlock the gates, although the guard dogs seemed to have accepted that as we brought gifts, we were okay. Here we all unloaded. The gangster indicated that his land went as far as the eye could see. I don't think I ever registered his name, though he must have filled in a form on the stand. Doru explained later that the motorway complex we'd passed was built on land he had sold.

"Not sure how many of his enemies are buried in the concrete. Quite possibly some are," he added, seriously.

We carried on discussing the sheep situation. Again trying to impress on the man that his enclosed area could be used for rams going in with ewes (to keep some pure and cross others) then later be made available for lambing. He seemed to understand, inferring he could do absolutely anything. He also volunteered the prospect of erecting a quarantine building, in order for our sheep to be sent to him for dispersal to other purchasers. While EU money was still subsidising these projects at that time, this man didn't seem short of personal finance. While we looked at the sheep he was on the phone. Doru translated: The Gangster would like us to eat with him in his restaurant that night and was ringing to tell the staff to cancel all other bookings. We would have the restaurant to ourselves.

We travelled on, meeting up as usual with the Romanian shepherds. We looked at the lambs, some of which had never connected with their mothers. We got Doru to explain this to The Gangster, who seemed surprised this problem could be solved as easily as by halting the progress of the flock. Sadly, we weren't convinced his shepherd would take it on board.

After several hours looking at sheep all over his very large farm, and viewing his immense fishing lake, basking in the warm afternoon sun, we eventually left via both security gates. The dogs were lying half asleep in the shade, aware of our departure, but thankfully not bothered. As evening approached we drove back several kilometres to a little village nestled in the hills. Grazing in a paddock alongside the drive to the restaurant were two beautiful Haflinger ponies, their golden coats and long cream manes and tails burnished by the rays of the sun, slowly setting between the trees. A mystical scene was created.

Both the meal and undivided service were amazing, although it did seem a little strange being the only customers in the building.

After all this, we never heard from him again. Whether he changed his mind or his enemies caught up with him, we'll never know.

Chapter Forty
In the Public Eye

A few years ago, Farmers Guardian started the British Farming Awards, 'searching for farmers who have made their business a success through innovation, determination, grit and foresight.' That first year, when I saw there was a category for Innovative Sheep Farmer, I nominated Aubrey.

"Don't be so daft," he said. "There's lots of farmers out there done far more than I have."

"Maybe. But lots of them have started with more than you did. There can't be that many sheep farmers who started with nothing who now run a 200 ewe pedigree flock, sell direct to returning customers and have built up a fantastic export market."

"Oh, do what you like," he said, shrugging his shoulders. So I did.

The main question on the entry form was 'What innovations has the individual introduced to the farm business?' I wrote about Aubrey's ventures into expanding the business by exporting Texels. I described his belief in the breed as a top class terminal sire and his aims to improve the quality of meat lambs produced from indigenous breeds world-wide. I explained how we secured interest from St Helena, through to Swiss and French contacts, the Abu Dhabi deal and our trips to Romania.

I pointed out that commercial farmers in the UK looked for

the biggest and strongest of the rams. Pedigree breeders sought the same with the females. While we were selling to both these markets, like most other breeders our lesser animals often ended up as top quality meat lambs. Once we investigated the export market we realised the smaller, narrower headed sheep, often rejected by British farmers, were exactly what other countries required. Selling them the right sort of breeding sheep worked for the way they shepherded them. Aubrey expanded these export markets and they flourished. Interestingly once we took these on to shearling rams, our commercial farmers soon realised the benefits of this type and sales in UK increased as well.

I don't know which one of us was more amazed when we heard Aubrey was through to the final three and we were invited to the Grand Dinner and Presentations, held that year at Sixways Stadium, Worcester. I say invited in the loosest of terms as the cost of the evening was £70 a head!

Thinking outside the box I realised that Steve, who Aub had worked so closely with when he was Chief Executive of the Texel Society, was now Marks and Spencer's head of Agriculture and M & S were part sponsors of the event, so yes, we went to the ball!

It was glitter and glamour all evening. Each farming category had the three finalists there, with supporting family and friends. We were on a table with other nominees and the eventual winner of the Farm Diversification. They had opened a Farm Shop, with an on-site butchery for their own animals and now grew a wonderful array of vegetables, some quite exotic. All the nominees were great fun to chat with and we all joined in celebrating the winners.

Neither Aub nor I were surprised when the winner of Sheep Innovator of the Year was a young man, former Nuffield scholar, who raised 3000 New Zealand Romneys on his family farm. These were recorded for growth rate etc. and he was a worthy winner, although difficult to compare his base finance with ours! The other runner up, whose family were there in full support, was also breeding from New Zealand bloodlines.

Such a memorable evening, where we met up with many friends and Aubrey came away with a framed certificate as Runner Up in the section. I thought it was a great achievement as when the winner was announced, the presenter said while competition throughout had been fierce, this section had drawn the most nominations.

At a later date, completely out of the blue we had a phone call from the BBC, Radio 4. At first I thought it was a joke, but he was most adamant. The agricultural advisor for The Archers was seeking advice for a young farmer starting out with a flock of Texels.

Over the course of the next few weeks both Aubrey and I had several chats about the planned purchase. They wouldn't reveal which character was going into them, but as we don't follow the Archers these days, it wouldn't have meant much anyway.

We asked what the new entrant wanted to do with the sheep and like many who come to buy breeding stock from us, the researcher hadn't really thought it through in that aspect. We tried to determine if he was going to breed pedigree Texel rams to sell to commercial farmers, simply breed some show sheep or a bit of each. We discussed the pros and cons of buying at sales, this being an obvious place to start. Buying in lamb ewes or starting with their own ewes and chosen ram and whether buying older stock that knew the job would be sensible.

Apparently, they took most of this on board because a friend who listens avidly, enlightened me on Ed Grundy's dabble in the breed.

Countryfile has visited us twice. Their first visit combined looking at commercial ram production with an animal osteopath, who was to treat a ram with a 'damaged shoulder'.

From a scenic point of view, we decided to take the crew across a number of freshly cut and baled hay fields to show off the wonderful Cotswold hills bathed in afternoon sunshine, where we had collected a large group of commercial rams. A convoy of range rovers drove down over the banks at speed, with most of the film crew balanced precariously on the back, fooling around like naughty schoolboys, pretending they were at Alton Towers!

We brought out a ram for the osteopath to look at, who diagnosed a slight shoulder injury. The crew spent a considerable time filming from many different angles, with long shots, taking in the background scenery to close ups of the actual treatment. We began to imagine our sheep starring in an epic movie, but when shown on the programme it took barely two minutes. We had not been aware that the ram had previously had a problem, but after treatment it was a good week before he walked sound again!

The crew said ours was one of the best visits ever, especially after the equally precarious return trip when they sat in the garden drinking tea and eating fruit cake.

Their second visit, some years later, was filmed in the yard and buildings where the quad bike was kept. After a spell of farm machinery thefts with two quads stolen, we were already in regular touch with the rural crime squad.

On one of these occasions, when the officer was explaining all we should do to prevent items being stolen, I said we'd solve the problem by wiring the barn door up to the mains and if anyone touched it they'd be electrocuted. He was horrified and told me I could not do any such thing. I assured him I could.

"Once we've buried the body in the muck-heap who would know he'd visited? His mates wouldn't be coming around, saying he had been to our place to nick a bike and gone missing."

Before I was arrested, Aub intervened, saying I was obviously joking, although he knew I was deadly serious. It had taken us almost a lifetime to be able to afford the quad and we had no intention of lying down quietly while it was stolen again.

When Countryfile came to film and report on the build-up of rural crime we only had a handful of crew, unlike the previous occasion when we had a full film set.

The man chosen to illustrate how a criminal could sneak in and pinch the quad could not ride it, so Aub had to don a black top and balaclava and steal his own bike, leaving the barn and yard at a most impressive speed. It looked truly authentic when we viewed our next two minutes on TV.

Chapter Forty-One
Weddings, Shows and Kiev

Heather and I had had great fun the previous autumn looking at a variety of wedding venues, and luckily Kevin agreed on the one we liked most. Their wedding was arranged for early February, close to the start of lambing. As we synchronise the ewes, I anticipated they would not start until two days after the wedding, so had no worries about leaving Mark T in charge while we attended the ceremony and stayed overnight.

Our son Mark had married Kate three years earlier and their reception was held in a marquee at the farm. Their August wedding was wonderful. The sun shone, though Kate and her bridesmaids did encounter a few raindrops as they ran the short distance from her parents' home to Bisley church. Guests were greeted at the reception with champagne and canapés and a brilliant group of street buskers.

Instantly the bride and bridesmaids threw their flowers to the crowd, joined hands and danced in a lively circle to the fantastic fiddles. Even before the meal started everyone was enjoying the country-fete atmosphere.

Planning a winter wedding for Heather and Kevin's day was quite different, but also delightful. Held under one roof there were no weather worries, but the sun did shine softly for the outside photographs. Over eighty friends and family were welcomed to the ceremony held in a magnificent oak-beamed barn. Heather radiated beauty as she stood next to her husband-to-be with their little son, Leo, acting as ring bearer.

Again, there was champagne and canapés, another wonderful meal with amusing speeches then dancing into the small hours. Our happy couple were not leaving for their honeymoon until the following day so most of the family stayed overnight at the venue. After a large gathering for a good breakfast we drove home.

We arrived back at the farm to find poor Mark T and his fiancé looking as though they hadn't slept for a week. They proudly showed us the ten ewes that had already lambed!

The wedding wasn't the only event to disrupt lambing. We also had to fit in a trip to the Ukraine.

The previous autumn we'd had a surprise request to represent both the Texel Society and our own flock at an agricultural exhibition in Kiev, in the Ukraine. I initially dismissed this out of hand as the exhibition was held in February, then realised the dates fell between two lots of synchronised lambing.

"Shall we?" I asked Aub.

"If our staff are happy to take over, why not? I'd like a break in the middle of lambing," Aub said. So we agreed to take part.

The weather during and just after lambing, was a bonus that year. Even though it was so bitterly cold that the grass was tinged with blue on top of the hills, it was dry. Our lambing staff were happy to be abandoned once things had quietened down and we flew to Kiev.

Thinking it would be even colder, I bought some sheepskin-lined boots only to discover it was a good deal warmer in Kiev than at home – this in spite of the fact that there had been considerable snowfall judging by the brown tinged piles of snow at the sides of the roads. On the drive from the airport we saw the iced-over River Dnieper, with fishermen risking their lives to catch fish through the circles they had cut in the ice. Apparently, a number lose their lives each year as the thickness of the ice is so variable. Sadly, money is scarce and some need to fish to feed their families.

Our hotel was in the city centre next to a government building with armed guards outside. Quite daunting. However, the hotel was smart and clean and we had a great room with all the required facilities.

It was good to be able to see something of the city while we were there. Along with other British representatives, we were driven a fair distance daily, through the city, to the exhibition, which was open from nine to four, with interesting lunches provided by our hosts. Those representing pigs and cattle felt there would little or no interest shown in sheep, but the result was completely the opposite. There were numerous sensible requests, although we were still at stalemate with any protocol to send direct to the Ukraine. Once this is resolved we have a number of contacts wishing to buy breeding stock.

Corruption was rife in the country. Our interpreters, two young doctors, had re-organised their schedules in order to accompany us daily. We paid more than they normally earned. One explained he had been lucky to obtain a grant to train with the benefit of a job at the hospital when he qualified. Unfortunately his wife, also a doctor, did not achieve a grant and had to pay for her training plus an additional sum to secure a job at the hospital.

"Why do you stay?" I asked, knowing a qualified doctor would be much sought after in most places, including England.

"I want to treat my own people," was his heart-warming answer. He knew the problems, but he was coping. He also explained about some of the recent riots in Kiev, which we had seen televised, where students had attempted a peaceful demonstration to challenge the government about conditions and money. Those in opposition had been infiltrated into the crowds and shots were fired on both sides, ending up in many casualties and fatalities of students, with the latter being blamed.

In the evenings we walked around Kiev. On our way to recommended restaurants we saw some of the wonderful churches with their gold-leaf domes illuminated by spotlights. A Ukrainian friend of a colleague also took us to a traditional eatery one evening, where the meal of several courses was delicious.

Several farmers calling on the stand invited us to visit their farms and we attempted to arrange this, but the authorities running the exhibition were horrified. They assured us the roads were very bad outside the city after the heavy snowfalls and vehicles may not be safe. We soon realised they meant nothing was safe there.

On our final day we took a sightseeing tour of the city before our flight home. The architecture was immense, but many parts of the communist history were frightening. We were shown the tall office building where the KGB could see right across the city and all the way to the Siberian plains, checking who was arriving and leaving. On that day there were parts of Kiev we were unable to visit, with roads barricaded due to another demonstration. Though a great experience, it felt good to be returning to our Cotswold farm.

That summer my first invitation was to judge the Blue Texels at the Balmoral (Royal Ulster) Show in Northern Ireland, now held on the demolished site of the Maze prison. This was the largest of their shows, hence a real honour to be invited, and we flew over for two days.

The classes were not huge, but the quality of sheep was good. In the shearling ewe class, I was immediately struck by a lovely gimmer entering the ring. She had all the attributes I looked for: great conformation, colouring, quality and presence. After handling and inspecting the class she was my first prize winner and I anticipated she may well be my Champion. The ewe lamb class was also won by the same breeder, again with a lovely lamb, but overall the males forward could not reach the same heights as the females, who won the Championship.

Having allowed ourselves time to watch the white Texel classes, we were amazed by the size of the lambs, so early in the year. Ours at home would never match them, but Aubrey assured me they would all be the same size in the autumn.

We watched competitions in the main ring while lunching in the members marquee, then took in several other sheep and cattle classes before completing our visit with a look at the H block building remaining on the site. Nothing much to see, but still a historic monument.

Looking back on the year we wondered how we crammed in everything. We were invited to more weddings, none similar in any way; other than each was most memorable and great fun. The summer weather was with us on most occasions. Between us we judged at four more shows and exhibited successfully at another four before the sales season took hold again.

The Three Counties show was hot. The sun simmered, extending rays so intense the grass crisped on receipt of it. There was no breeze. Not a murmur. The sky was an idyllic blue without a cloud in sight, not even a whisper of white fluff.

Like others, we continually checked the sheep in the marquee were in the shade, hoping a small breeze would rise to flow through their pens. The sheep were happy enough. Wherever they were, this sun would be burning down on them, the only difference being their shade came from canvas rather than trees. Thank goodness it had not been this hot the previous day when we were out showing in the ring.

The showground at Malvern lies in a basin below the Malvern Hills and hosts its own weather system. Some years it would rain, others we could think it was snowing, with the wind stripping flowers from the lime trees leaving a white carpet wherever they fell. But this year the wind was dormant.

Aub adjusted one outer wall of the marquee so it cast a further shadow over our pens, without stopping the very slight breeze just beginning to move the air.

Aub's trips to the National sales were with us again and he disappeared while I sorted rams to take to sales. As a result of our Kiev visit we had a request to entertain and accommodate Andrii, a pleasant young Ukranian who ran a farm breeding unit for a company. His trip was sponsored by the company, for him to learn about Texels and AI and to visit a sale. I persuaded the organisers that a three week stay would be far too long, but we welcomed him for a week, incorporating a show, artificial insemination of ewes and a visit to the main Builth ram sale, the biggest ram sale in the world. He was incredibly impressed

I think we almost killed him with work, although we did not ask him to do anything more than help us. He could not believe that we did everything ourselves, assuring us he had three women to milk their handful of goats and three men to look after twenty sheep. I gathered he simply did the paperwork. I am not sure how much he gained from his visit, but he took many photographs to show his boss who was financing him. The day after a hectic two days at the ram sales he could not get out of bed until lunchtime, so we suggested he spent his final two days sightseeing in London, explaining to his organisation that we had sudden family commitments that made this more practical. He was most relieved.

Chapter Forty-Two

On Dogs

Without a working dog, a sheep-farmer is nothing. Even when we farmed a pocket handkerchief of land, the arrival of Annie made us realise there is no better or more efficient way to move sheep than with a trained dog.

Hill farmers learned of their importance many generations ago. Trained to obey commands and whistles, their greatest attribute is their natural herding instinct and innate common sense. Gathering sheep from the tops of the fells would be impossible without them and it is their responsibility to bring in every last sheep. Instinct often takes over from instructions. Any number of men on quad bikes cannot do the work of a good sheepdog.

We have had some wonderful dogs and each death broke my heart. After Annie, came one of her puppies whom we had sold to a neighbouring farmer. Ness had shown all the signs of a sharp little sheepdog before she left us, keen and enthusiastic. A few months later we were asked to have her back as the man was leaving his present job. Ness spent the next few months attached to me as if by glue. She was terrified of sheep and any newspaper or magazine we picked up. What he had done to her we never discovered, but she lived with us for the rest of her life, eventually re-trusting Aubrey as well. A real family pet, in her last few years she became known as Dear Old Dog.

Another local shepherd, who had retained too many pups, gave us Nell. One of the best. She was partially-trained and her natural instinct did the rest, a brilliant sheepdog in any situation and like all our dogs, kind, friendly and completely trustworthy with children. Buried on a hill top overlooking the main sheep meadows, she lies where she loved best.

Kim came to us when a friend finished shepherding and found Kim could not settle without sheep. She accepted us immediately as we were less important than her work, which was her passion. Not in the first flush of youth when she came, she worked then retired with us for another six years.

Mist was also a gift. Arriving as a bouncy puppy just prior to lambing, she drove us insane with her curiosity but matured into a wonderfully talented dog. Although she worked for both of us, she was always Aubrey's dog as Ness had been mine.

Sending Mist off around the sheep one morning, when low cloud made it impossible to see any distance on our Cotswold hills, Aub ended up on a search and discovered her lying by a ewe who was stuck on her back. Mist knew there was a problem and that if she didn't return, Aub would come and sort it out. Those brains you cannot explain.

Daisy was definitely mine. Beautiful, with a long black and white coat and remarkably small brain. She never made a sheepdog, though she followed me round the farm religiously. She allowed me to move sheep better than if I'd been alone and was obedient enough to lie in a gateway and turn sheep, while not taking an active part. She adored me and I adored her. I often felt neither of us was more than adequate at our jobs but it really didn't matter.

When Mist passed away, Daisy's lack of use became even more apparent, but finding a good dog is never easy. Jill was a cast off when her owner went out of sheep, passing the farm to his daughter.

"She won't work for a woman," she said. "She doesn't like them."

I ignored Jilly for the first week, simply feeding her each evening when I fed Daisy in the adjacent kennel. Initially she stood to the back of the run, watching as I put her food down. I told her she was a very good girl. Gradually, without either of us really noticing, she accepted me and today works for us both, joins in with family life and is still our main star. She is adored by our grandchildren who call her 'Lilybicket', the cry that went out when she gently, but firmly, stole a biscuit from a small child's hand.

Sadly, Daisy's life was shortened by mammary cancer. I was devastated. Jilly was used to working alone, as Daisy had not been a great help, but she still missed the companionship. It was twelve months before I considered finding another dog. Then there was Maisie. Black and white, short coated, with the most expressive tan eyebrows.

Maisie, the apprentice, lives to work sheep. If we could bottle Maisie's joie de vivre each morning and sell it, we would make our fortune. She greets me with a love so deep I feel guilty for having left her alone all night, although she has been in the best place. Her kennel and run are safe and warm, she's well fed and watered, but oh how she would love to spend the night in bed with me.

She will squeak and whimper as soon as she sees me open the front door, then bounces on her hind legs like a demented spring. Tigger comes to mind. I always let Jill out first, so she can have my undivided attention and cuddles before Maisie erupts. When her kennel door is opened, she leaps to kiss my face and ears, although we are now reaching a better understanding of greeting at floor level. I do not think we have ever had a dog with so much enthusiasm for life, although her greatest love is the sheep. She generously obeys my commands, but when sent off with Aub, returns far too quickly to have completed the job. If he calls her to go on the quad she leaps aboard, but should I be staying in the yard, she's off again in one swift movement. If I mount the quad she's instantly glued to my side in the box until I direct her elsewhere. Her love is unconditional and holds no criticism. I don't think I've ever experienced quite this relationship with a dog.

Chapter Forty-Three
A Lifetime's Dream

A visit to New Zealand was something Aubrey and I had discussed and endeavoured to be able to afford for many years.

In the background, behind all the sheep activity, we had also bred and produced a number of Miserden Sports Horses. One of these, a great favourite of mine with talent to burn and plenty of attitude, had taunted me for a long time. Objectionable to break in, he narrowly avoided being shot by miraculously improving his dangerous behaviour overnight; but this breakthrough did not last. Sold twice, he came back both times for performing like a manic idiot once he left our yard, only to show that butter wouldn't melt in his mouth once he returned. Convinced it was the place rather than people he disliked, we found he was better in a large yard, so lent him to a friend with a livery stable where her daughter competed him successfully. When her mother suggested it was time to sell him, it took me completely by surprise. He went to a young girl to event and did not come back. The proceeds of his sale were so unexpected, we decided it was time for the New Zealand trip.

We planned to take a month from mid-November to mid-December when all the ewes should be safely in lamb and the stock easily managed. Mark T was prepared to check and feed twice a day and we were leaving Jill with him, as he might need her.

Maisie was another problem. Now just over twelve months old, her brain was far too active for her to be put into kennels and become bored rigid. I approached one of the top sheepdog trainers in the country who lives close by to see if he would continue her training while we were away. He agreed to see her, but needed to assess her capabilities. Fortunately she passed her audition and was welcomed onto his farm for the duration of our trip.

Comforted by the fact our sheep and dogs were in safe hands and a friend would check the cat daily, we felt ready for our adventure.

On a thirty-six-hour stopover in Hong Kong we took in the sights on two fantastic excursions. Next we were greeted in Auckland airport by Anne Marie, a great friend who emigrated there some years ago, and after early supper in glorious sunshine on the Auckland quay we parted company. Anne Marie had horses entered at Karaka racehorse sales. We were to meet up there in a few days.

Having left me to organise our trip, Aub was slightly suspicious when we joined the Kiwi Experience student bus heading for Paihia and Cape Reinga at the top of North Island at seven the following morning.

"Why are we doing this?" he asked. "And why do I have to get up at six o'clock in the morning? I'm on holiday."

"It'll be fine. You wait and see. It means you can look at the scenery and not have to drive."

He need not have worried. Our international companions, although mostly under twenty-five, welcomed us into their group.

Our driver was a great tour guide, pointing out places of interest as we drove through Auckland: amusingly full of himself and convinced Kiwis were the best in the world. Best at Rugby, best at yachting, best at everything. When we wandered down to a small river after a morning coffee and pie break, we were greeted by a huge duck, chest puffed out, non-stop quacking. Obviously a Kiwi and the best duck in the world!

For that first stop in Paihia I had booked a room in a small hotel opposite the student accommodation, but we joined the others for a barbeque that night.

Vegetation was sub-tropical, with giant ferns and palms lining the route north to Cape Reinga. The torrid mix of currents where the Pacific and the Tasman sea meet was spectacular. Sand boarding was the highlight of the return trip, and a couple of young students from the Netherlands were obviously impressed when they realised we would be joining in. The bus drove along a creek below some massive sand dunes where we took our boards, walked up the sand mountains, the wind driving hard against us. Not quite the thrill of tobogganing on snow at home, as the soft sand resisted too much speed, but a great experience.

Just thirty minutes from central Auckland, Karaka Racehorse sales are one of the biggest in the world.

We met Anne Marie again at the Ready to Run sales for two-year olds, where she had three entered, two for clients, one her own. With her husband and sons, they run a top breeding stud and sell worldwide. The 600-seat auction ring was surrounded by extensive gardens, parade rings, dining areas and of course stables. It was a wonderful opportunity to see all this, enhanced by Anne Marie's own horse making double the money she had anticipated.

After several days at their farm, admiring horses and cattle, we headed off for Hawkes Bay, then Masterton to meet up with other friends and on to Wellington. The crossing from North to South Island was magical, low sun reflecting on the water; the scenery spectacular.

With four weeks of wall to wall sunshine, both North and South Island sweltering in a heat-wave, perhaps we didn't see the country at its most lush, but we certainly enjoyed it. Nor did we see many sheep although there were a few Merinos in South Island. Tremendous irrigation machines swept across the drying land, and dairy cows and bulls were everywhere.

Lack of organisation on my part meant we missed a major NZ Texel sale by just a week, but we did manage to visit several breeders, seeing some pedigree stock bred from British semen, which were far superior to some of the other stock. Time was not endless and Queenstown was the furthest south we went before flying back to Auckland from quake-damaged Christchurch, for one last evening with Anne Marie and friends. Our first Christmas party was a barbeque!

We returned to Britain at its worst. Flying directly back with just a four-hour stopover at Hong Kong was a bad mistake as neither of us slept well on the flight. Our son Mark picked us up from Heathrow where depressing grey heaps of dirty snow decorated the roads home.

Because the weather had been so wonderful, it was easy to forget how bad it was at home. Cold, wet and snow had taken their toll. Pneumonia had killed two good ram lambs while we were away, both destined to be retained as breeding stock.

Christmas was almost upon us. Drinks parties and dinner invitations made life bearable, but neither of us was eager to return to work. With a month away from the physical demands of sheep-farming it took a little time to regain the necessary enthusiasm.

Maisie returned a better-educated dog. Though she'd settled well to her training she was delighted to be home again.

Lambing was hard and the weather unkind. Thank goodness we were now in a position to employ at least two experienced lambing staff, with other occasional help. But there were still many cold hours when we worked so hard to bring life into the world and keep it alive.

The first group of lambs were out when the forecast for the Beast from the East attracted attention. Aubrey was as tired and fed-up with being back at work as I was, but unlike me he refused to believe that such bad weather was coming in.

"Since the bloody gales of '87 they've had to over react. We often have snow," he said.

"I know. You're probably right. Could you just move the big bales around by the New Shed, so the wind doesn't come through so badly there, just in case the water freezes?"

"It'll be fine."

The bales were not moved, the wind howled in and the water froze for almost a week. We were lambing the second lot when the major blizzards came, demanding that all the lambs would benefit from being somewhere sheltered, preferably inside. Our main lambing assistants had moved on to other flocks, as by now the work load had usually eased. Not so this time. With the weather as it was, it was hell. Sheep sheds bedded up in the evening looked like scenes from Dr Zhivago the following morning, ewes in lambing pens were shrouded by inches of silken snow; their lambs luckily snuggled under them.

Our new neighbours, recently moved in from London, proved to be life-savers. They appeared on Saturday morning bearing hot bacon butties and proceeded to bed-up every barn in use. This in itself was wonderful, but the night brought yet another storm, and the following day these guardian angels repeated the ritual. It is hard to explain how daunting it is to face the thought of bedding up yet again when you're exhausted. I think, at that point, they saved our lives, and obviously are now our very good friends.

Farming has always been our dream. Summer does eventually return with warmth, green fields full of healthy lambs, skylarks and blue skies, but by the end of March my enthusiasm was waning. When I reached our bed at nights I could have cried. My body ached so much. Every limb felt sore and tired. I remember thinking 'if I die during the night I won't have to go through all this again tomorrow'.

The singles in the bottom fields would have to survive, with ample hay, hard food twice a day and water troughs kept working – which was a feat in itself. Ewes with younger lambs were brought into small spaces, far too cramped, at nights. Some coated with ice, their small bodies insulated by the lanolin in their wool. So thankful of warm dry nights, they kept in family units with no mis-mothering.

By now I had collected over twenty-five lambs to feed, a fair number whose mothers had such badly chapped teats they wouldn't let their babies suck. They also needed treatment themselves. Thankfully, some lambs took warm milk from a machine with teats, but several seemed to have no idea how to suck a bottle or machine. The kitchen looked as though we'd been burgled and I hadn't even the strength to fill and put on the dishwasher. I needed to decide whether I vacuumed the sitting room or baled it.

For several years Aub had been trying to persuade me we needed a Gator, an agricultural version of a golf buggy, with windscreen and doors and even a heater! Feeding outside in the winter blasts on a quad could be hard-going. Luckily in January we'd agreed to buy one and even better, it came with a cab on the back for the dogs. Feeding through these horrendous weeks was made bearable for everyone because of our new machine, which at weekends could be piled high with feed and dogs. Not to mention grandchildren, the only ones still enjoying the snow.

When the very last ewe lambs the relief is immense. Especially if she's had two good lambs, loves them and milks on both sides. Several complete nights' sleep almost clears the mind.

Spring eventually arrived. The snowdrops were late to appear, and no doubt wished they hadn't when more snow fell on them, but now there was a haze of yellow from daffodils and primroses and the pale green foliage of the hawthorn. Although still cold, magnolia and blossom trees had started to burst into bloom and the flowering currant in the garden was serenaded by bees harvesting the early pollen. We still suffered the occasional snowstorm, harsh and unnecessary, but the longer days were becoming warmer and the sunshine more frequent.

Show schedules dropped through the letter box, alerting us that summer was just around the corner. The copper beech trees changed from soft pink to darker red. Farming friends phoned to arrange meeting for a drink or meal now lambing was finally over. There was still plenty to do. Treatments and vaccinations for lambs, the sheep needed foot-trimming and shearing and there was fertilizer to go on to assist with grass growth.

As the spring days moved into summer, there was no better life than being a farmer. Those last few winter months had tested our strength, but the summer certainly compensated. The show sheep were sheared earlier than the main flock, but there was now adequate room for these to be housed at night, should the weather suffer a relapse. The main ewe flock would not be sheared until early June, as the fleece protected their udders from cold winds that could still cut across the hills and cause chapped teats or mastitis.

The lambs were doing well, basking in the warm sun. It was great weather for livestock, grass and crops. When the grass grows, so do the lambs.

While show entries were completed in April, it was often not until the beginning of June that we selected the sheep for the Three Counties. We always have some idea which older sheep will be our stars and select them earlier for shearing, but occasionally it still takes long hard decisions to pick out what we hope will be winners. The lambs may still be on their mothers, but will be weaned just before the show. We will make a short list of those going, but final selections still take earnest discussion.

Later in the year we visit the Royal Welsh, although rarely taking sheep these days. Five days away in July is difficult to arrange and often the weather is so hot the sheep do not appreciate staying in the warm buildings. But an overnight stay, allowing us time to catch up with friends and watch both the Texel and Blue Texel judging is great fun. Many friends have caravans on the cool of the hill, a wonderful place to crash at the end of the day, sharing fantastic barbeques, talking and drinking far too much.

Our dreams of farming took a long time to materialise, but we have achieved more than I ever imagined. Our son, who runs an IT firm as a living, has just purchased one hundred acres and several farm buildings in the next village. The dream goes on, though I feel he will finance his dream more quickly than we may have.

Little did we know when we took possession of Satan, that aptly-named Black Welsh Mountain demon, how our farming careers would pan out.

About the Author

Sue Andrews is a journalist and sheep farmer. She has written for county magazines and the national equestrian and farming press.

She and her husband Aubrey are established breeders of both Texel and Blue Texel sheep. Their close involvement with the work of both Breed Societies has taken them all over Europe. Their prize-winning Miserden Texel sheep have been successfully exhibited at major shows up and down the country.

They have two children and they farm in Gloucestershire.

Acknowledgements

My grateful thanks to Lorna Gray of Crumps Barn Studio, for her enthusiasm, advice and editorial skills.

To Aubrey for encouraging me to finish this book. And to both Aubrey and Steve, previous Chief Executive of the Texel Society, for their anecdotes, amusing memories and useful information about their trips together.

To Mary Griese, MA in creative writing at Bath Spa, who has read endless chapters, offered suggestions and supported me all the way. And Sharon Walker, whose final proof read was invaluable.

To all our farming friends, both local and countrywide, without whom this adventure would not have been so enjoyable. And to our landlords and ladies, past and present, for enabling the dreams to evolve.

And finally to all those involved with Texel sheep; other breeders, those in the office and everyone who has been part of the enormous social spectrum. Thank you.